MAN ON EARTH

How Civilization and Technology Changed the Face of the World - A Survey from Space

CHARLES SHEFFIELD

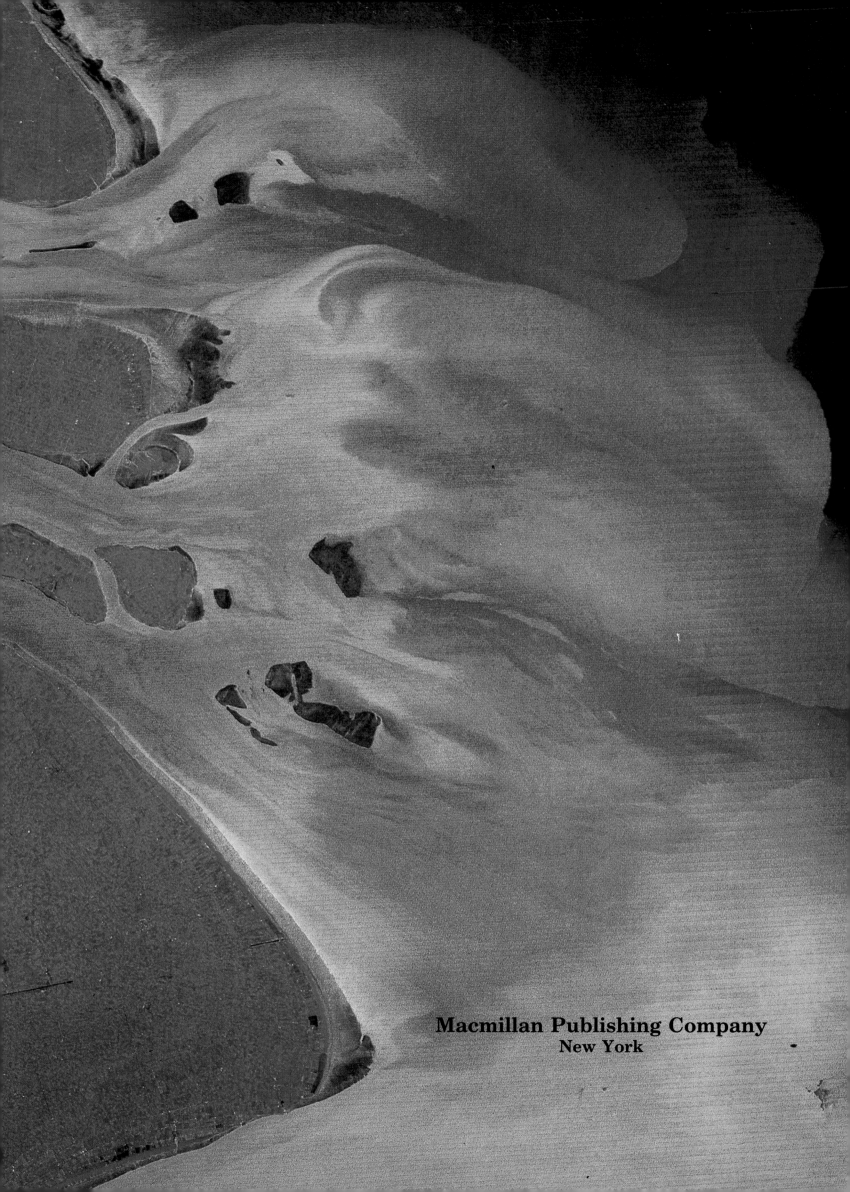

Macmillan Publishing Company
New York

To Bob and Mollie Zall

Author's Note Throughout the book, metric tonnes (1,000 kilograms, or 2,204 lbs) are used. For most purposes, the difference between this and the United Kingdom or long ton of 2,240 lbs is negligible. Gallons are imperial gallons, 20 per cent larger than the U.S. gallon.

In text descriptions, 'top', 'bottom', 'left', and 'right' refer to these directions *as the book is held for reading,* rather than with respect to the usual way of reading a map, with north defined as the top. North arrows associated with each image allow compass directions to be identified where these are referred to in the text.

Page 1: K2 (Mount Godwin Austen)
Pages 2-3: Shanghai and the Yangtze

Design by Paul Watkins

Maps by John Flower

Copyright©1983 by Charles Sheffield, GEOPIC, Earth Satellite Corporation and Sidgwick and Jackson Limited

Macmillan Publishing Company
866 Third Avenue, New York, N.Y. 10022

Library of Congress Catalog Card Number: 83-804

ISBN 0-02-610100-9

First American edition 1983

The photograph of the Landsat spacecraft on p.7 is reproduced courtesy of the U.S. National Aeronautics and Space Administration. The detail image on p.136 is reproduced courtesy of the French Centre National d'Études Spatiales, Digital Simulation File courtesy G.D.T.A. All other images copyright GEOPIC, Earth Satellite Corporation.

Printed in Italy by New Interlitho SpA Milan

Acknowledgements Many sources and individuals have contributed to the content of this book. I would like to thank particularly Linda Zall for her help in all phases of image selection, evaluation and description; Max Miller, Ron Hodge, Betty Hall, Brian Hollen, Carl Selsky, and Larry Norris for photographic consultation and image production, and John Hunter and Byron Loubert, who produced miracles of colour balance and colour manipulation upon request; Mike Place and Kawana Estep for assistance in development of special enhancement algorithms and for computer processing of images; Martha Williams for assistance with figures and layout; Osamu Takano, John Everett, Orville Russell, Jon Dykstra, Ira Merin, Bill Brooner, Rich Michael and Steve Prucha for discussions of particular scenes; and Jane Heller who again led production from original idea to final book.

Many of the images presented here were available only because of the enthusiastic co-operation of remote sensing organizations and Landsat receiving stations around the world. I would like to thank the EROS Data Center of the U.S. Geological Survey; the Resource Planning Unit of the World Bank; the Canadian Center for Remote Sensing; the South African Council for Scientific and Industrial Research and National Institute for Telecommunications Research; the Brazilian Instituto de Pesquisas Espaciais (I.N.P.E.); the European Earthnet Programme Office; and the Landsat receiving stations at Fucino, Italy, and Kiruna, Sweden. Each of these groups provided me with the loan of computer tapes and helpful suggestions on scenes of interest. Finally, I would like to recognize my debt to earlier U.S. Government works on the Landsat system and images, in particular the volume *Mission to Earth* by Nick Short, Paul Lowman and Stan Freden of N.A.S.A.'s Goddard Space Flight Center.

Contents

Introduction

Pictures of the earth taken from space have now been available for more than twenty years. They began in 1960 with the first black and white images produced by the TIROS-1 weather satellite and were soon followed by colour photographs taken by the hand-held cameras of the *Gemini* and *Apollo* astronauts. To most observers the fascination of these pictures was the opportunity they provided to see the world 'in the round' for the first time, as a majestic blue-grey sphere, floating cloud-cloaked against a backdrop of stars. Detail of the surface, comparable with that provided by high-flying aircraft, appeared less interesting, something that would be useful only for purposes of military surveillance.

It was not until the late 1960s that other unique advantages of space images became apparent as a means for monitoring the condition of the earth's surface. The first satellite designed specifically for such purposes was launched by N.A.S.A. on 23 July 1972. Known originally as ERTS-1, and later as Landsat-1, that spacecraft is shown opposite. Its objectives: to monitor the resources of the whole earth, and man's activities on the earth, on a regular, widespread basis, and under uniform observing conditions.

Landsat-1 was designed to produce images allowing us to assess the relationship between man and the planet he lives on. It would show the effects of man on the environment, monitor the activities of mankind, and serve the needs of man by measuring the earth's natural resources. This book provides graphic proof that Landsat and its successor spacecraft have satisfied the wishes of its designers, probably beyond their expectations; and although aesthetic appeal of the spacecraft image products was never any part of the design criteria, the pictures provided by Landsat often have elements of beauty and mystery.

Since that first launch there has been continuous imaging of the earth's surface by a series of Landsat spacecraft. Landsat-2 was launched in January 1975, Landsat-3 in March 1978, and the most recent and most advanced spacecraft, Landsat-4, in July 1982. Together, these satellites have returned hundreds of thousands of images that blanket the earth from latitude 81 degrees north to 81 degrees south. Flying at a height of 917 kilometres (570 miles), each spacecraft returns more than a million separate items of information to the earth *each second,* every day of the year. In the time that it takes to read this sentence, 10,000 square kilometres (4,000 square miles) of new data have been recorded.

It would be quite impractical to record this great mass of data on film on board the spacecraft and then return it to earth in that form. Instead, the operation is wholly electronic. Powered by solar panels, the spacecraft's electronic imaging system converts observed light intensities to numbers, in the form of discrete electric impulses. These numbers are transmitted to a network of receiving stations as a continuous digital radio signal, to be recorded there on magnetic tape, and to provide an archive of information unique to a particular time and ground location. From the tapes, computers convert the stored numerical values to an image format, from which film products are finally created. This is the first point at which the Landsat data are seen as a 'picture' in the conventional sense of the word. A single Landsat scene covers a ground area of more than 33,000 square kilometres (13,000 square miles), and more than 30 million numbers must be processed before the image can be created.

Fourteen Landsat receiving stations are now in operation around the world, three in the U.S.A., two in Canada, two in South America (Brazil and Argentina), two in Europe (Italy and Sweden), one in Africa (South Africa), three in Asia (Thailand, India, and Japan), and one in Australia. Landsat-4 can also return data to the earth through a pair of communication relay satellites, located in a much higher orbit 35,000 kilometres (22,000 miles) above the equator.

The earth resources spacecraft were never designed to compete with photographs from aircraft. In comparison with the latter, they offer only a coarse image, allowing individual features to be seen down to about the size of a football field (or a tennis court, in the case of the higher resolution system of Landsat-4). While an aerial photograph will often permit the study of objects less than a metre across, Landsat's value lies elsewhere, in the uniform, repeated coverage that permits continuous evaluation and re-evaluation of the changing condition of any parcel of land, almost anywhere on earth. Each Landsat spacecraft provides repeat coverage of the same area every eighteen days, at the same local time of day (about 9.30 in the morning). Although the orbit around the world is almost an exact circle, when traced on a Mercator projection of the earth the ground track of the satellite's motion appears as the series of S-shaped curves as shown in the diagram opposite. The Landsat sensors always provide pictures at the same scale, under illumination conditions that vary only as the angle of the sun above the horizon changes with the seasons.

This steady, unvarying series of images, each covering an area 185 kilometres (115 miles) square, contributes greatly to mankind's continuing efforts to explore, develop and monitor our planet. Farmers and agronomists all around the world now watch the steady development of crops as the growing season progresses, monitoring growth, detecting early signs of drought and disease, and assessing probable production. Hydrologists observe the growth and shrinkage of snow cover in inaccessible mountain ranges as autumn advances to winter and then to spring, and they can predict the flooding of swollen rivers by estimating snow melt. Foresters compute the area of cut timber, assess changes in land use patterns, and see early evidence of the onset of insect disease.

To the geologist, constantly driven to search for fuel and minerals in more and more difficult terrain, Landsat data offer a unique prospecting tool, permitting a preliminary assessment of geological structure, lithology, fracture patterns, and mineral-bearing potential before embarking on the first field trip. The same images provide information about the terrain, and assist in planning that field trip through extreme desert, across arctic plains, and over high mountain ranges. Environmentalists, concerned about the steady loss of arable land to desert, or the erosion of precious topsoil, monitor these changes, year by year, and evaluate different techniques for their arrest. Economists and planners track the growth of urban areas, the success or failure of water pollution and waste disposal programmes, and the changing patterns of land use of a mobile population. In the developing world, governments and international assistance agencies use the same data source to control over-grazing, relocate population, choose sites for dams and reservoirs, and assess the potential of undeveloped lands. To all these users, earth resources satellites have become an indispensable tool, providing data at a small fraction of the cost of any other source.

All this information is not derived without an accompanying effort of interpretation. As a quick glance at the colours of the pictures in this book should make clear, the information sensed by the Landsat spacecraft differs substantially from that seen by the human eye. Blue light, readily visible to humans, is strongly scattered by the earth's atmosphere, so this wavelength is not recorded by the spacecraft. Instead, the imaging system views the earth in four different wavelength regions, two in the visible and two in the infra-red region of the spectrum (this has been increased to seven wavelength regions for the newest satellite, Landsat-4).

The two visible wavelengths correspond to what we see as red and as yellow light, but the human eye cannot see infra-red light at all. Since in addition we can see only three primary colours, while the spacecraft 'sees' four, the Landsat images – no matter how they are presented – will inevitably differ in their appearance from conventional colour photographs. Most of the presentations in this book are typical 'false-colour' images, in which the longer infra-red wavelength is shown as red, true red is shown as yellow, and true yellow is shown as blue. In such a presentation, crops and other vegetation usually appear as shades of red, urban areas as grey or grey-blue, clear deep water as black, and muddy or shallow water as various shades of blue. However, since confusion between types of ground cover on the basis of colour can be misleading, a good deal of experience is needed before reliable interpretation of the images can be performed.

The image on page 87, showing the San Rafael Swell of Utah, is displayed in a different colour presentation, one designed to enhance the differences between certain types of surface materials. This is just one of scores of alternative ways of presenting Landsat information, all with their own special advantages, but all calling for their own special training in image interpretation.

The discussion of the methods by which Landsat acquires image data of the earth, and the ways in which these data are processed to yield useful information, has been given here in very brief form. For a fuller description, particularly on the processing techniques and different image products that can be generated from Landsat data, the interested reader is referred to the volume *Earthwatch,* published in 1981, by the same author.

GROUND COVERAGE PATTERN OF THE LANDSAT SPACECRAFT

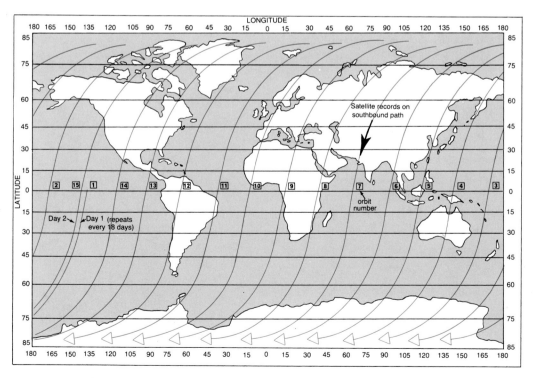

The Ancient World

In 4000 B.C. it is estimated that the total world population was no more than 100 million. By the birth of Christ this had certainly doubled, but not until about 1800 did the number of people on earth exceed 1,000 million. Two thousand million was reached about 1930; 3,000 million in 1960; and 4,000 million in 1975. Today's population is about 4,600 million. With present rates of growth, by the year 2000 the earth will struggle to support close to 6,500 million people.

At the same time, the amount of available energy per head of population has been increasing. One thousand years ago each person on earth controlled an energy budget equivalent to that obtained by burning at most 45 kilos (100 lbs) of coal a year. Today each person in the world uses that much every week, and in the United States and Europe consumption is considerably higher − each man, woman, or child uses the energy equivalent of 45 kilos of coal every day of the year.

If we use total available energy as some measure of man's potential to influence his environment, the earth today should be changing because of man's works a thousand times as fast as it changed two millennia ago; and the twin factors of population increase and energy use ought to dominate the effects of man on the present face of the globe.

The images presented in this book bear out that analysis. Most of the evidence of man seen on today's earth was created in the past 100 years, and not merely because the works of ancient civilization have crumbled with time, nor because the old building materials of stone and sun-baked brick are difficult to see against a background of natural surface rocks and sands. The Seven Wonders of the Ancient World were the Pyramids of Giza, the Tomb of King Mausolus at Halicarnassus, the Temple of Artemis at Ephesus, the Statue of Zeus at Olympia, the Colossus of Rhodes, the Pharos lighthouse, and the Hanging Gardens of Babylon. The largest of these, the Great Pyramid of Khufu (Cheops), was a stupendous engineering feat for the times (about 2600 B.C.), but it involved less than one-tenth of the mass of materials used to build the Aswan High Dam.

The ancient world is usually seen on Landsat images by association with particular locations, rather than through the visible evidence of monuments. Thus Rome, Vienna, Athens, Giza, Yogyakarta, Byzantium, Batavia, Naples, Paris, Hastings, Moscow, Jaffa, Samos, Heliopolis, Syene, and the Pillars of Hercules will all be found in this book (though not all in this chapter), but usually in association with more modern features, and often with their newer names − Cairo, Istanbul, Jakarta, Tel Aviv, Aswan, or Gibraltar.

The older parts of the ancient cities have often been replaced by modern buildings; in any event, old sections that have been preserved are usually unspectacular as images. Asphalt and concrete, the modern building materials, provide a brighter reflection of sunlight in both visible and infra-red light than do brick and clay. And the old development is often small, an ancient nucleus of buildings and narrow streets dwarfed by the broad boulevards and sprawling modern suburbs that surround it.

Athens and the Peloponnesian Peninsula

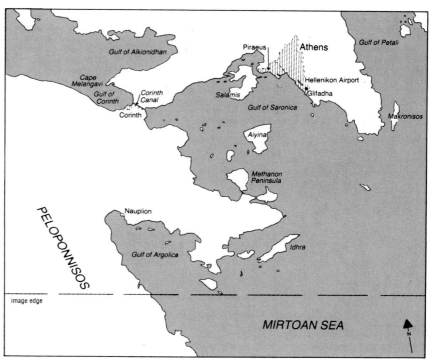

The August image overleaf displays clearly the harsh, dry terrain of the southern part of Greece, with the Gulf of Saronica at scene centre and part of the leaf-like outline of the Peloponnisos (formerly known as Morea, 'the mulberry leaf', because of its shape) to the lower left. Most of the scene is made up of the greys and browns of limestone hills, covered by scrub vegetation of broom, oleander, bay, myrtle, olive and kermes oak. The red-displayed coastal plain around Nauplion at the head of the Gulf of Argolica and the red coastal strip west of the narrow neck of the Isthmus of Corinth indicate extensive agriculture. The commercial crop is mainly fruit, with figs, oranges, olives, and grapes predominating ('currant' is derived from the word Corinth).

Greece and the Aegean Sea were a birthplace of Western civilization and the area is rich in history. Corinth itself has been an influence in Greek affairs since at least 650 B.C. It lies on the west side of the isthmus, just below the clearly visible straight line of the Corinth Canal. The canal was completed in 1893 and links the Gulf of Saronica with the Gulf of Corinth. North of the canal, the beak-like peninsula of Cape Melangavi juts west to separate the Gulf of Corinth from the Gulf of Alkionidhan.

The modern capital of Greece, Athens, is a city of 2.5 million people. It is visible with its ancient port of Piraeus as a large blue-grey area on the north-east shore of the Gulf of Saronica. The Hellenikon airport is the thin grey strip on the shore south-east of the city, close to the resort area of Glifadha. To the west of Athens lies the island of Salamis. The famous sea battle between the Greeks and Persians took place in 480 B.C., in the strait that lies between Salamis and Athens.

The island of Aiyina (Aegina) in the Gulf of Saronica south of Athens was also an important commercial power at the time of the Persian invasions of Greece. It introduced coinage to the Greek peninsula and was powerful enough to defeat Athens in sea battles during the sixth century B.C. The famous temple to Aphaea on Aiyina lies on the north part of the island. Agriculture (mainly figs, vines, and almonds) is confined to the lighter-toned area on the west side of the island. The east side shows as unvegetated bare rock.

Other prominent features of the scene include the island of Makronisos at the southern end of the Gulf of Petali; the near-island of Methanon, south of Aiyina and attached to the eastern mainland of the Peloponnisos by a narrow neck of land only about 100 metres wide; and the island of Idhra (Hydra) which, as its name suggests, was in ancient times well-watered and covered with trees, but which the image shows to be now rocky and sparsely vegetated.

Image scale and date: 1 cm = 3.7 km, August 1979.

Rome and Central Italy

This image covers the western part of central Italy, from the central Apennine mountains, seen here as bright red in the upper left of the scene, to the shores of the Tyrrhenian Sea. Rome, the capital of Italy and for many centuries the premier city of the Western world, forms the light blue patch at the lower centre of the picture.

Within the city a number of famous features can be identified. The mottled red area above the Tiber River to the right of the city is the Monte Palatino, the site of the Forum, the Colosseum, and the Circus Maximus, and is, according to tradition, the oldest settled part of Rome. Between it and the brighter red of the Villa Ada to the left is the Villa Borghese. Below the river, the red park of the Gianicolo and the Villa Doria Pamphili can be seen, and between them and the larger red wooded areas to the left the Vatican City is visible as a tiny square of red with a spot of brighter blue above it. The Isola Tiberina, in the middle of the city, can be seen as a discontinuity in the narrow dark thread of the river.

Near the Tiber's outflow to the sea at Fiumicino the crossed blue-grey runways of Rome's Leonardo da Vinci Airport are visible on the coastal plain. Further up the coastline is Anzio (formerly Antium), where in the spring of 1944 one of the most bitterly-fought engagements of the Second World War took place. Following the coast upwards on the image, the red

oblong of the Circeo National Park is clearly visible, with the isolated limestone mass of Monte Circeo forming the spur at the western end of the Golfo di Terracina. The blue-green Pontine Marshes, drained in the 1940s, lie just to the left of the park.

Four of Europe's five active volcanoes are in Italy, and it is clear from the image that this part of the country has been very active volcanically. Lakes fill the wide craters that run as a line north-west to south-east across the scene: Lago di Vico (Cimino) at the centre of the Monti Cimini on the bottom left of the image; further up and to the right, Lago di Bracciano in the great crater of the Sabatini Volcano; and halfway up, Lago di Albano in the crater of the Latian Volcano in the Colli Albani. The bright red vegetation surrounding the calderas demonstrates the fertilizing influence of decomposed volcanic materials. The famous 'seven hills' on which Rome is built are ridges of hardened volcanic ash.

Up in the Apennines, top left on the image, the great pinkish-red cultivated area of the Fucino Depression stands out from the natural vegetation of the mountains. This was Lago del Fucino until the nineteenth century, when between 1854 and 1875 the lake was drained and the land reclaimed. The road that runs through Pescina and Avezzano is clearly visible as a white thread just left of the planted area.

Image scale and date: 1 cm = 4.9 km, June 1975.

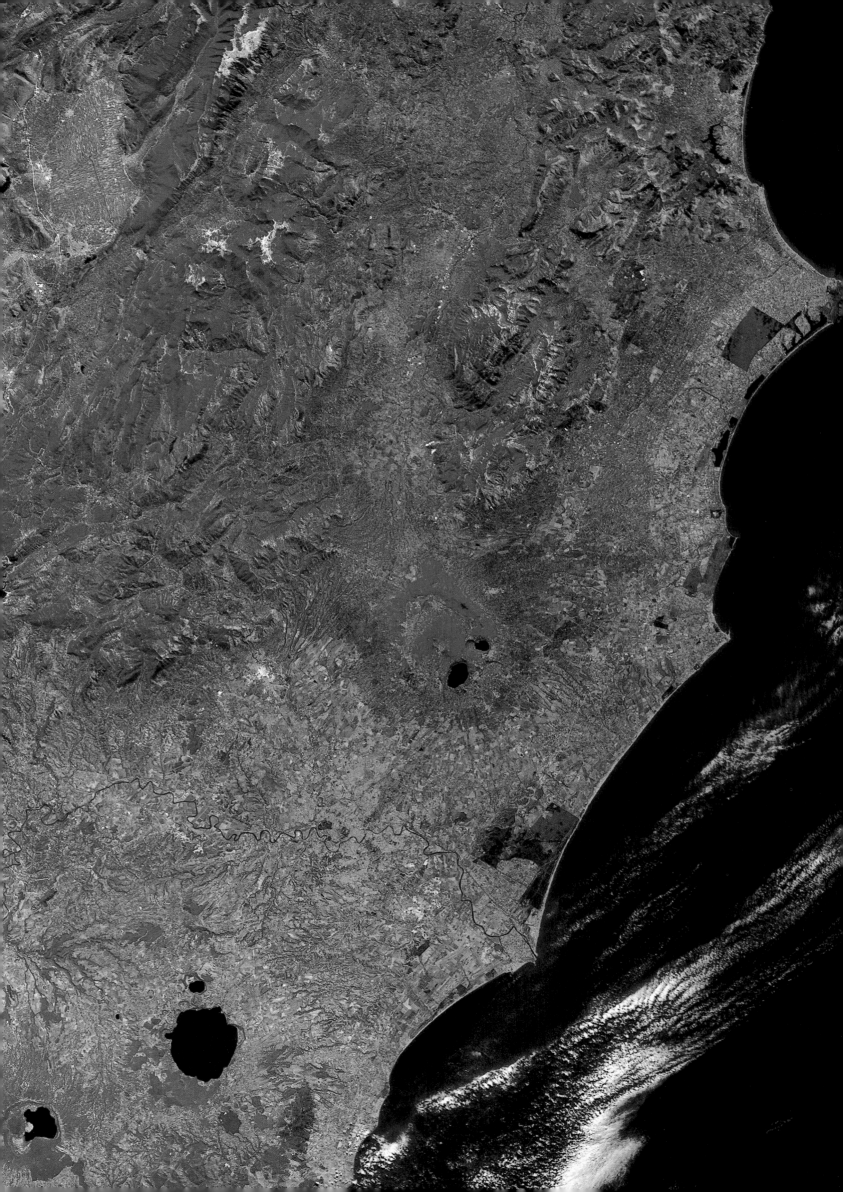

Istanbul and the Bosporus

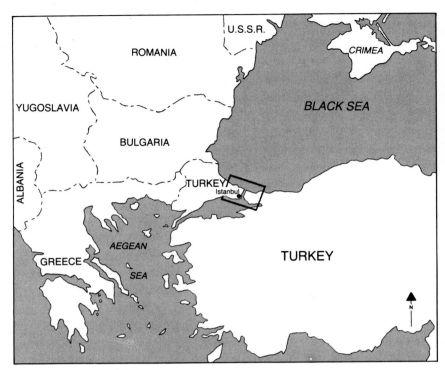

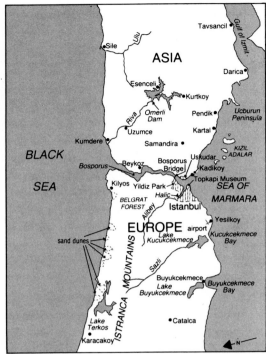

Before A.D. 330 Istanbul was Byzantium, capital of the eastern Roman Empire; then until 1453, when the city was captured by the Ottoman Turks, it was Constantinople. Since that time it has been known to the Turks as Istanbul, although Western use of that name came only in this century. The city stands on the Bosporus, the 30-kilometre (19-mile) long strait that connects the Black Sea and the Sea of Marmara to form a dividing line between Europe and Asia. As the only sea exit from the Black Sea the strait has been of great strategic importance for hundreds of years.

Istanbul, a city of over 3 million people, is the industrial and commercial centre of Turkey. The old city forms a triangle 23 square kilometres (9 square miles) in area at the Halic ('Golden Horn') inlet on the west side of the strait. At the tip of the promontory of the old city a small patch of red marks the gardens of the Palace of the Old Seraglio, now the Topkapi Museum. A line of scattered red dots below the museum, making an equilateral triangle with the Halic and the Sea of Marmara, shows the broken line of the old city wall, now grown over with vegetation. Greater Istanbul, nearly twenty times the size of the old city, extends far beyond this, although on the image it is not easy to distinguish between urban development and the surrounding blue-grey coastal plain. The city has grown along the sea coast towards the Yesilkoy Airport, clearly visible as a white linear pattern, and along the Bosporus halfway to the Black Sea. The Bosporus Bridge can be seen as a narrow grey line just to the left of the red area of Yildiz Park, on the western shore of the strait.

On the Black Sea coast, Lake Terkos shows as a large blue area. It has served to supply water to Istanbul since the end of the last century. Between Lake Terkos and Lake Buyukcekmece to the right runs a 180-metre (600-foot) ridge of hills that forms the base for the Catalca (Chatalja) defensive line of Istanbul, a line of mainly earthwork fortifications that protected the city from Western attack in the nineteenth century. Further up the image to the left the Belgrat Forest shows bright red; the white patches along the Black Sea coast are sand dunes.

On the eastern, or Anatolian, side of the Bosporus opposite Istanbul lie the cities of Uskudar (Scutari, formerly Chrysopolis) and Kadikoy (Chalkedon, from which the name of the quartz chalcedony is derived). The spidery dark area of the Omerli Reservoir can be seen inland. To the south, in the Sea of Marmara, lie the Princes' Islands, or Kizil Adalar, literally the 'Red Islands'. From top to bottom, the larger islands are Buyuk, Heybeli, Burgaz and Kinali; the summer homes of many Istanbul residents are located here. Further up, the Marmara shore runs past the point of the Ucburun Peninsula along to the Gulf of Izmit at the top right-hand corner of the image.

Image scale and date: 1 cm = 3.9 km, August 1979.

The Cyclades and Sporadhes Islands

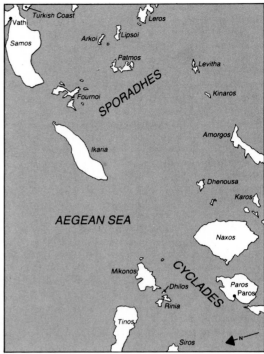

These islands, scattered through the warm southern Aegean between Greece and Crete, are perhaps thought of today mainly as holiday resorts; but 2,000 years ago they were seats of power and influence in the eastern Mediterranean.

Samos, in the upper left of the image, forms part of the Sporadhes, or Dodecanese Islands. It reached the zenith of its power in the sixth century B.C. It was the birthplace of Pythagoras (about 530 B.C.), and of the astronomer Aristarchus (about 270 B.C.), who proposed the first heliocentric theory for the earth. The present capital of Samos, Vathi, is visible as a blue spot on the deep bay top left. The island is covered with vegetation, displayed here as red, and is clearly very fertile. It produces olive oil, wine, silk, cotton and tobacco. Below it lies Ikaria (Nikaria), also well vegetated.

The southerly islands of the chain are clearly much less fertile, and several show only the grey of uncovered rocks. Patmos, right of Samos, is volcanic, bare, and desolate, and was used as the place of banishment by the Emperor of Rome, Domitian, for St John the Evangelist in A.D 80. A monastery was later located there but the island remains almost uninhabited.

Continuing down and right on the image, the large island at the lower right centre is Naxos (formerly Dia), the largest and most fertile of the Cyclades group. It played an important part in the wars between the Greeks and Persians, and was conquered by Persia in 490 B.C. Today it is rich in fruit trees,

and exports wine, corn, olive oil, and especially the hard abrasive mineral emery, which has been mined there since ancient times (Pliny and other Roman writers called this substance *naxium*). Directly below Naxos is Paros, the source in ancient times of the famous Parian marble, a translucent white stone used by Praxiteles and other Greek sculptors. It is clearly a less vegetated and fertile island than Naxos, and is actually composed of a single mountain rising from the Aegean. The capital, Paros, is on the bottom bay of the island.

To the left of Paros lie Mikonos, Tinos, and Siros. The long, narrow island of Dhilos can be seen off the lower end of Mikonos. According to ancient Greek beliefs, this island formed the centre of the Cyclades, and the Temple of Apollo, built there in the fourth century B.C., was a major shrine. Today the island is uninhabited. Mikonos and Dhilos are composed of igneous rocks, which weather to soils of podzolic type. Most of the rest of the Cyclades and Sporadhes are made of metamorphic rocks, weathering to red-brown Mediterranean soils of more fertile type. Thus Mikonos and Dhilos carry very little vegetative cover, in addition to displaying different rock colour.

The earliest dates for continuous habitation of most of the islands seen in this image are unknown. However, it is likely that all settlements on them must be more recent than about 1470 B.C., when the volcanic explosion of the island of Thira (Santorini), just a few miles off the image to the south, inundated this area with massive tidal waves.

Image scale and date: 1 cm = 6 km, June 1981.

Cairo and the Nile Delta

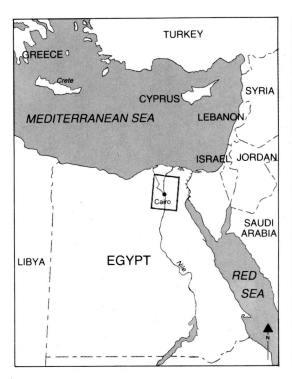

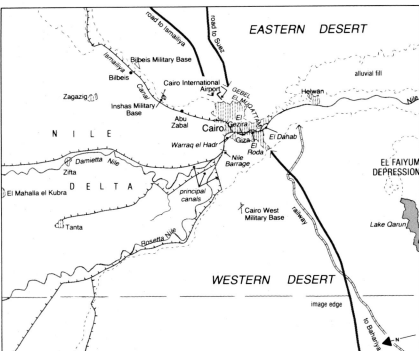

The total agricultural land in Egypt's 1,000,000 square kilometre area (386,000 square miles) is less than 39,000 square kilometres (15,000 square miles). The area of the Nile Delta, which shows red on the image overleaf, is about 18,000 square kilometres (7,000 square miles). Its importance to the economy of the country can hardly be overstated.

The black thread of the Nile River winds its way north through an irrigated valley that has changed little in appearance for more than 6,000 years. A few kilometres to the left of Cairo, which is visible as the large blue area at the head of the delta, the river divides into the Rosetta Nile and the Damietta Nile, which then flow about 65 kilometres (40 miles) to meet the Mediterranean. At their intersection is the Nile Barrage, the control system for the flow of water throughout the delta. A number of the principal canals can be seen as straight dark lines left of the barrage. Within the main delta the blue urban areas of Zagazig, Zifta, Tanta, and El Mahalla el Kubra are clearly visible, each of them a city of more than 100,000 people. The principal crop of the delta is cotton, followed by corn and clover. Since the annual rainfall is only a few centimetres, every acre must be irrigated for production.

Cairo is the largest city in Africa, with a population approaching 5 million. Its international airport, and the white line of the road leading to it, are just visible above and to the left of the city. Above Cairo on the image lie the dark cliffs of Gebel el Muqattam. The roads and railways that run off the top of the picture to Suez and to Ismailiya appear as dark lines cutting through the Eastern (Arabian) Desert. Also clearly visible is the dark line of the road and canal that run through the left-hand side of Cairo to the blue area of Abu Zabal, past the dark forks of the airstrips of Inshas Military Base to Bilbeis, where the Bilbeis

Military Base is visible just off the delta area, and then on to Ismailiya. In the Nile River, as it runs through the city, lie, from left to right, the islands of Warraq el Hadr, El Gezira, El Roda, and El Dahab. Warraq el Hadr is a bright red vegetated area without urban development. El Gezira (literally 'The Island' in Arabic) lies just to the right, with the pink oblong of public gardens and sporting club grounds visible amid the blue of city development. El Roda, further right again, is also urban, and measurements of the annual level of the Nile have been made from there for more than 1,200 years. The fourth island, El Dahab, shows no urban development and is variable in size depending on the level of the Nile.

Below Cairo on the image, stretching down from the Nile towards the desert, lies the blue area of Giza, itself a city of 700,000 people. Just right of Giza are found the 4,500-year-old Great Pyramids and Sphinx (not distinguishable on the image). Twenty kilometres (12 miles) south of Cairo, on the banks of the Nile, the blue area of the city of Helwan can be seen. Once famous for its sulphur springs, it is now an industrial centre, with power stations and steel and cement works. The road and railway to the Bahariya Oasis (off the image to the south-west) are clear light lines in the lower right of the image, running through the tans and browns of the Western Desert. Above Helwan lie bright white areas of alluvial fill, and beyond them the winding white courses of numerous dry wadis.

At the lower right of the image is Lake Qarun, lying in the El Faiyum Depression. El Faiyum is believed to have been created by wind erosion. At its deepest point it lies about 45 metres (150 feet) below sea-level, and extensive agriculture can be seen extending from the lake almost to the River Nile.

Image scale and date: 1 cm = 3.9 km, May 1978.

Eastern Java

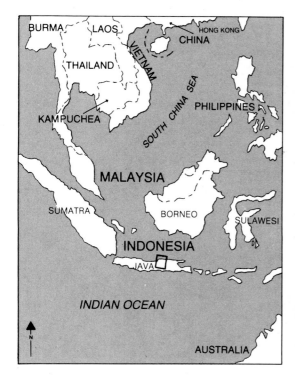

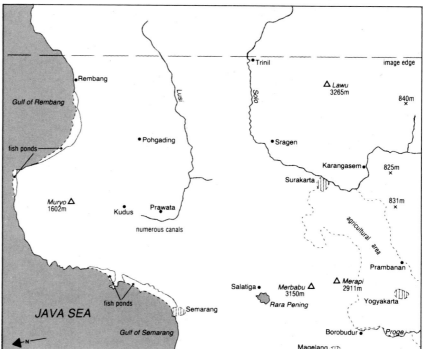

The whole of Europe contains only five active volcanoes; the island of Java alone has at least thirty-five. Given this degree of volcanic activity, one would not hold out much hope for the preservation of ancient Javanese monuments unless, like Pompeii and Herculaneum, they had been completely buried in ash and lava; but, contrary to expectation, some of the world's most famous and exquisite ancient Buddhist temples lie within this image area.

The city of Yogyakarta, home of about 400,000 people, is visible as a dark-green patch to the lower right of the scene on pages 24–5. Long regarded as the cultural and spiritual centre of Indonesia, Yogyakarta served as the capital of the revolutionary government during the fight for independence in the late 1940s. Left of the city lies the active volcano Mount Merapi, with greenish lava flows visible on its south-west slopes, and beyond it stands the taller peak of Mount Merbabu. The famous temple of Borobudur lies below and to the right of Merapi, near the bottom edge of the image. Although it is very large, at least 230 metres (750 feet) square, it is not easily distinguished on the picture from other cleared areas of earth.

One of the foremost Buddhist temple monuments in the world, Borobudur was built in about A.D. 850 but was covered with soil for hundreds of years, either by natural causes or to protect it from the Mohammedan influences that took control of the island after A.D. 1400. Built around a natural mound of earth, the great stupa and its surrounding carved walls were rediscovered and dug clear by the British governor,

Sir Stamford Raffles, in the early nineteenth century. Sixteen kilometres (10 miles) east of Yogyakarta lies Prambanan, the home of other famous antiquities. The *Tjandi Sewu* (Thousand Temples) is here, mostly dating from the eighth century. Prambanan and Borobudur contain the greatest monuments of ancient Java and attract visitors from all over the world.

This area of Java can also lay claim to antiquities far older than anything seen at Borobudur; for it was at Trinil, not visible but right on the top edge of the image on the Solo River, that the first bones of *Pithecanthropus erectus,* Java Man, were discovered by Eugene Dubois in 1891.

At the top of the great swath of speckled red agricultural land which begins at the bottom right of the image, the city of Surakarta is visible as a dark patch. At the top of the scene the vegetated red peak and volcanic cone of Mount Lawu (3,265 metres; 10,712 feet) stands out from the surrounding plains, while Mount Muryo forms the striking headland at the left of the picture. The major city of Semarang (population, 650,000) lies on the bay below and to the right of Mount Muryo. The headland is flanked by fish ponds, seen as offshore patterns of grey-green dots and fine lines on the image. The white areas near image centre and further right (other than obvious clouds near the mountain peaks) are cleared agricultural lands, principally for rice. All Java suffers tremendous overpopulation, with great pressure on all arable land for multiple cropping. The white areas along the coast, however, represent unproductive soils.

Image scale and date: 1 cm = 3.9 km, September 1972.

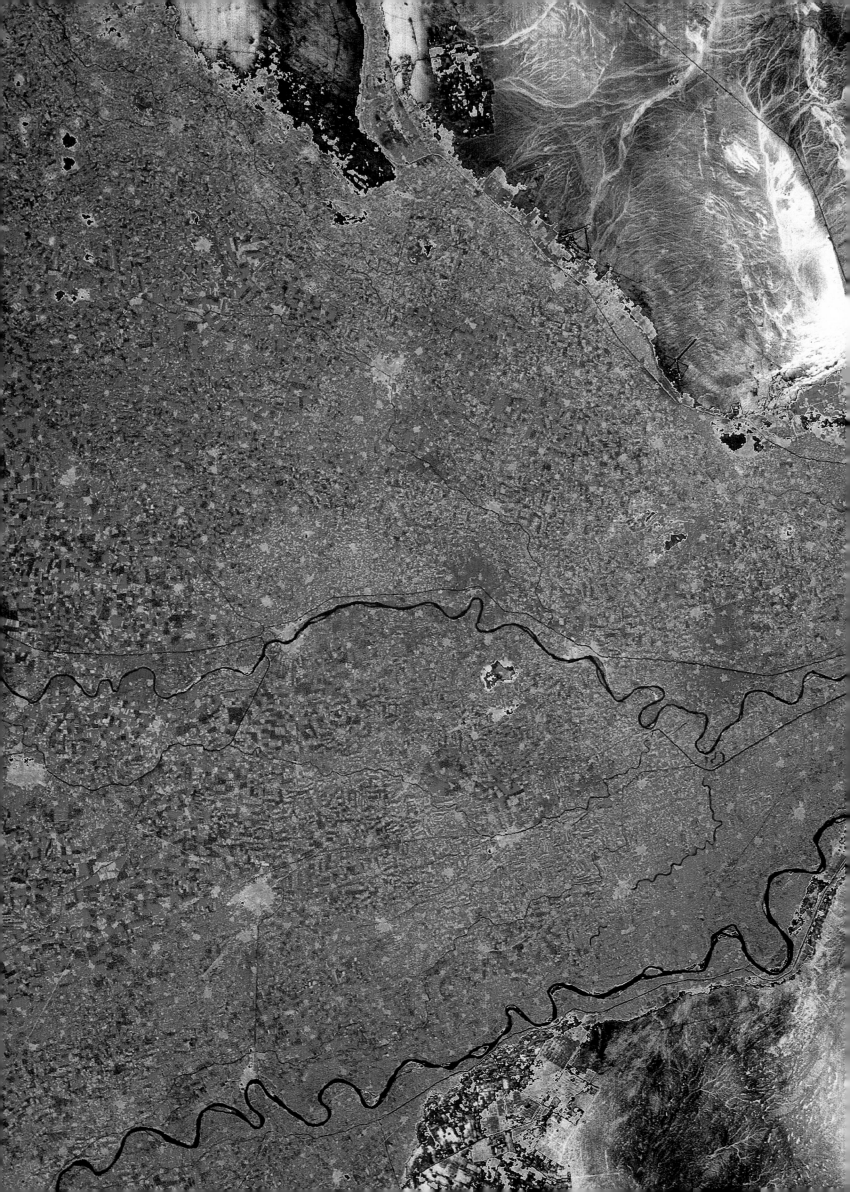

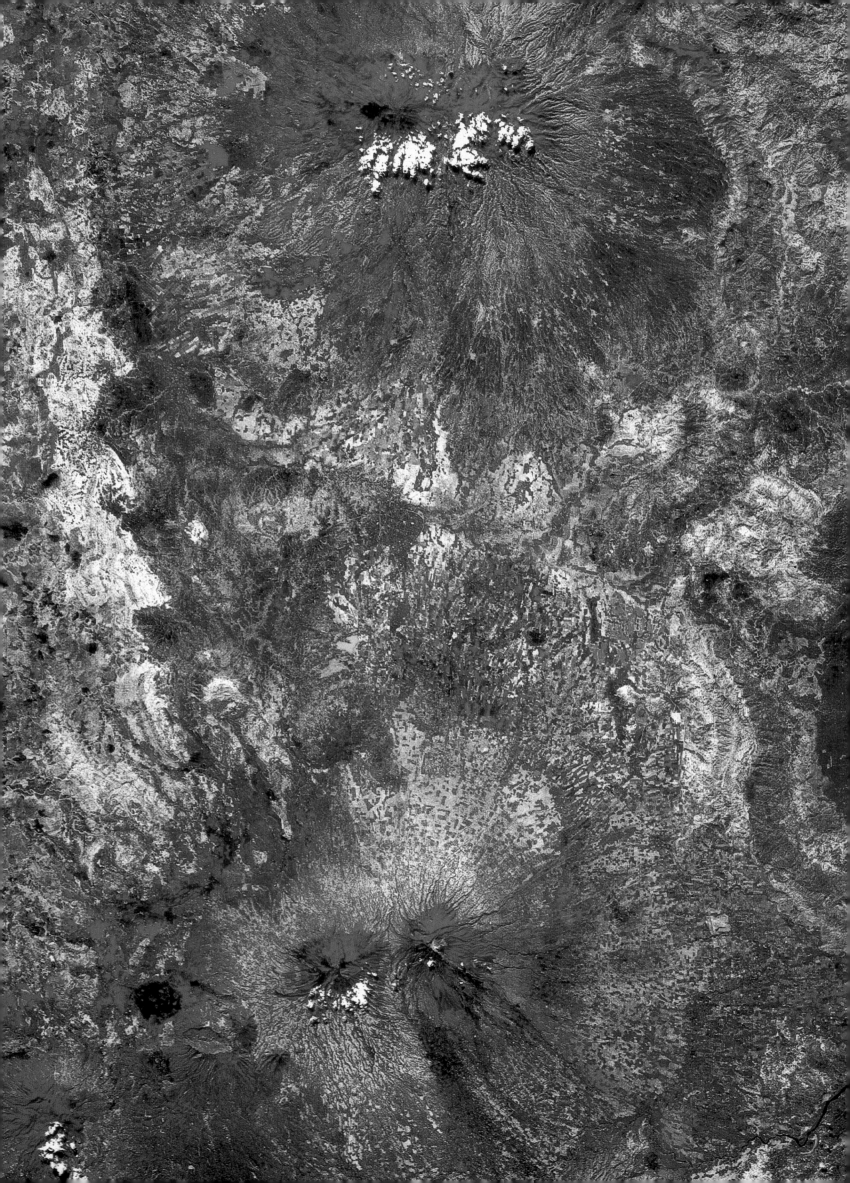

Shaping the Earth

Mankind has been changing the face of the earth since before the beginnings of written history, but not always for the better.

Seven thousand years ago much of the Sahara Desert teemed with plant and animal life. Oaks, limes and alders grew on the grassy uplands, and giraffes, elephants, ostriches and gazelles roamed among them. Early man assisted the spread of the world's greatest desert by cutting trees along the western coast of Africa. One thousand years ago, much of Europe was primaeval forest. The need for wood as fuel and construction material gradually turned France, Britain and Germany to lands of field and pasture. Three hundred years ago, the draining of the English Fens directed by the Dutch engineer Cornelius Vermuyden yielded a deep, peaty soil ideal for agriculture. Today most of that peat has vanished, and an infertile substrate is now the surface soil.

Before we conclude that our ancestors were foolish and naive we should look at more recent cases. Seventy years ago the central plains of North America seemed like an endlessly productive region, one giant field which would grow crop after crop of grain with no need for fertilizer. But once ploughed, the mat of grass roots that held the topsoil in place was gone within a generation; by the 1930s much of Oklahoma and Kansas had become dust bowls, dry and unproductive. Within the last twenty years, roads built on Alaskan permafrost have increased the absorbed heat of the surface, leading to melting of the underlying permafrost and to rapid disintegration of the road. Today, the tropical forests of Brazil are being cleared at more than 1 per cent per year, to satisfy the need for fuel and new agricultural land. But the cleared land is not fertile; the jungle soils lack humus and essential minerals, and are quickly dried out and washed away.

Some effects of man's actions are less visibly obvious. The great irrigation scheme for El Gezira, shown on pages 114–15, has undoubtedly increased the productivity of central Sudan, apparently without decreasing soil fertility or causing soil loss. However, slowly flowing water through El Gezira's great system of canals has proved to be an ideal breeding ground for the tiny snails that carry bilharzia, a debilitating disease that is now endemic through the region.

In all the above cases, an apparently rational development effort has produced undesirable side effects; and today more than ever mankind has the tools for planetary engineering, for causing changes to the earth's surface on an unprecedented scale. But as the scope of the projects increases, so does the need for careful planning and monitoring if potentially disastrous side effects are to be avoided.

A generation ago, information collection costs for monitoring very large areas were prohibitive. Now observations from spacecraft provide us with the necessary inexpensive data. Sources of building materials can be located, transportation routes defined, geological structure determined (important if dams and reservoirs are to be constructed), and changes in land use mapped as they occur. Still more important, this remotely sensed information often allows us to estimate long-term effects while the work is at the design stage. For the first time, we are in a position to make realistic trade-offs between near-term benefits and future costs.

IJsselmeer

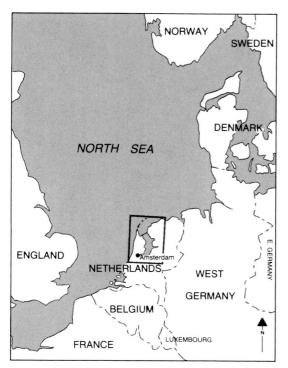

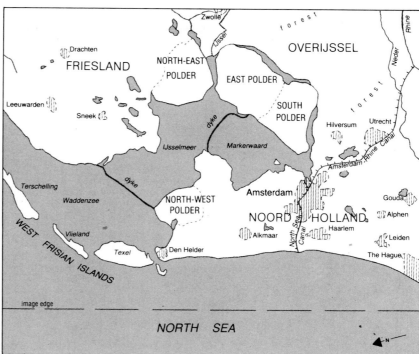

The image overleaf displays one of the world's most extraordinary feats of modern long-term engineering: the reclamation of much of the Netherlands from the North Sea. Flooding of the central area of this image took place in the thirteenth century after the North Sea breached protective offshore sandbars and swept in to form the Zuider Zee and the West Frisian Islands of Texel, Vlieland, Terschelling, and Ameland (just off the image).

The reclamation effort has proceeded steadily through the years. The long dyke, clearly visible as a white line on the left side of the image, was completed in 1932, and the Zuider Zee, no longer a sea but a lake, was then renamed the IJsselmeer. Locks, constructed to permit the continued passage of barges, are visible as breaks in the narrow white line of the dyke as it bridges the mouth of the IJsselmeer. The North-west Polder, a greener area just to the right of the main dyke, was drained from 1927 to 1930; the North-east Polder at the top of the IJsselmeer was drained from 1927 to 1942; the East Polder from 1950 to 1957; and the South Polder from 1957 to 1968. Although the South Polder was only recently reclaimed, large areas of red vegetation are already visible within it. The water area known as the Markerwaard, to the right of another long curved

dyke, is now being drained and will be completely reclaimed before the year 2000. Since the whole of the Netherlands is close to or below sea-level, most of the land shown on this image must be continuously drained, and the famous network of Dutch canals is visible as narrow dark lines running through the fields.

At the right-hand corner of the Markerwaard lies Amsterdam, the capital of the Netherlands and a city of 1 million people. The urban area shows blue-grey, with docks clearly visible to the right of the North Sea Canal. The cities of Leiden and Utrecht stand out clearly as blue patches against the surrounding red agricultural countryside. The Hague, seat of government for the Netherlands, lies on the coast at the lower right-hand edge of the image area. The large dark-red areas above Amsterdam and running off the top of the scene are forests.

The West Frisian Islands are edged with white sandy beaches. They are steadily being eroded on their seaward shores. The lighter blue shallow waters of the Waddenzee separate them from the mainland province of Friesland, whose capital and principal market town, Leeuwarden, is plainly visible a few kilometres from the shoreline.

Image scale and date: 1 cm = 3.8 km, August 1978.

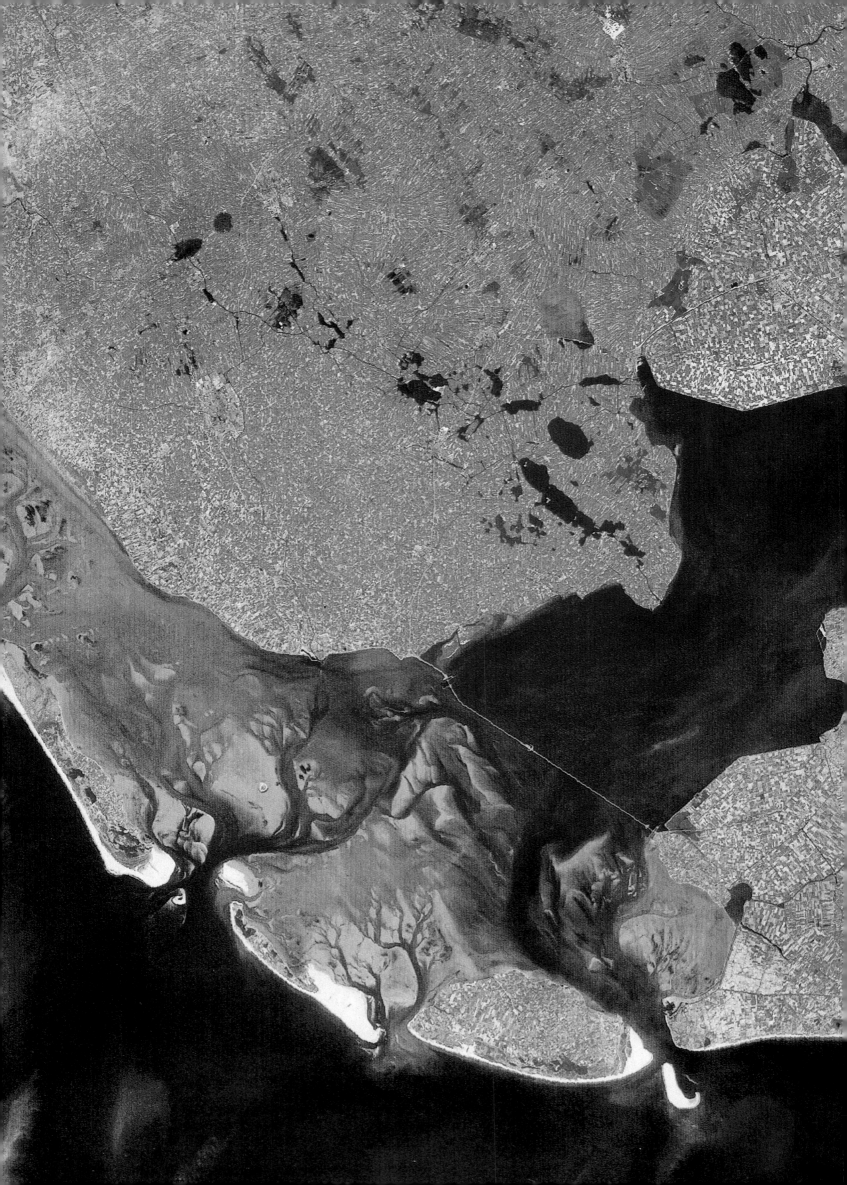

The Keban Dam, Turkey

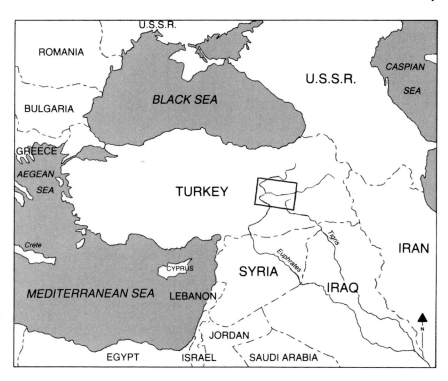
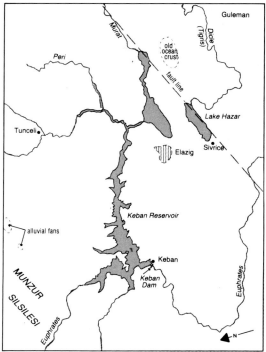

For the past twenty years the Turkish State Hydraulic Development Agency has been engaged on a systematic programme for increased provision of electricity throughout the country. The result of one part of the programme can be seen on this image. This is the Keban Dam across the Murat and the Euphrates (known in Turkey as the Firat) Rivers in eastern Turkey. Begun in 1964 and first brought into commission in late 1974, the dam is 205 metres (673 feet) high, 1,100 metres (3,600 feet) long, and provides 1,200 megawatts of electrical power. Its planned final capacity will be almost three times that, at 3,500 megawatts.

The structure of the dam is clearly visible here as a light bar blocking the lower right-hand of the long drowned river valley which forms the Keban Reservoir. The Euphrates River can be seen as it curves down and to the right and then runs along the far edge of the scene. Further south along the river, off the image area, two other great dams, the Karakaya and the Ataturk, are now under construction.

This region sits at the border between central and eastern Anatolia, in a harsh and rugged terrain that forms part of the Taurus Mountains. The range known as the Munzur Silsilesi runs to the left of the dam, and flat beige patches of alluvial fans are visible on the extreme left of the lower portion of the red vegetated area. This area has in the past been volcanically very active, and although the mountains offer poor soil, the river valley of the Murat is a rich alluvial soil of decomposed lava. The rough, broken countryside of east-central Anatolia is the most sparsely settled part of Turkey despite workable deposits of chromite at Guleman (in the top right of the image, though not visible) and of lead and zinc at Keban.

A closer examination of the geology of the area makes one wonder about the wisdom of placing a major dam and reservoir here. Earthquakes are frequent throughout Turkey, and this area in particular is seismically active. The clear line of a major geological fault can be seen running south-west to north-east across the upper right quadrant of the image, through Lake Hazar and on to the upper river valley of the Murat. This is the meeting place of two great tectonic plates. The Anatolide Plate, the more northern of the two, is being slowly squeezed west by pressure from the lower Arabian Platform, which is moving north and sliding under the Anatolide Plate. The two plates came into contact about 15 million years ago; before that there was ocean between them. A remnant of old ocean crust is visible on the image as a bluish-grey oval to the right of the lighter blue broadening of the Murat River. The movement along the fault line is only a few centimetres a year, but this is enough to be directly measured without difficulty.

The Keban Dam holds back 40,000 million tonnes of water. Eastern Turkey suffered earthquake tremors that registered 6.9 on the Richter Scale in 1966, and 6.8 in 1975. A disturbance of this magnitude near to the dam could fracture its limestone foundations and send a huge wall of water downstream along the Euphrates valley.

Image scale and date: 1 cm = 5.1 km, July 1976.

The Mississippi Delta

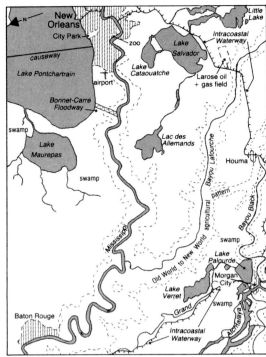

'Father of Waters' and 'Great River' to the American Indians, the Mississippi with its principal tributary, the Missouri, stretches the length of America from northern Minnesota to the Gulf of Mexico. This image shows the 6,000-kilometre (3,730-mile) river in its last sinuous section, 145 kilometres (90 miles) before it meets the gulf.

The numerous meanders and oxbows make it clear that the river flows across a great alluvial plain of its own making, a plain that covers the whole image area and extends hundreds of kilometres north of it, up to the confluence with the Ohio River. The light-blue tone of the water shows that silt continues to flow down to the Gulf of Mexico, enlarging the delta. An estimated million tonnes of solids a day is carried down by the river. The Mississippi has always been subject to periodic flooding, and the clean lines of its banks indicate man-made levees. These must be continuously maintained and straightened, at the same time as the river is dredged and de-silted.

On the banks of the river and along the Bayou Lafourche on the right-hand side of the scene, broad pink strips of agricultural land are visible. Close inspection shows that the field patterns run in long, thin lines, directly away from the water. This is the 'long lot' or 'Napoleonic' system of riparian land division, and it points to an early French influence in the region. The principal crops are rice, sugar cane, cotton, and corn. The brighter reds bordering much of the agriculture indicate pasture and low-lying woodlands, and the dark grey-green in the lower right of the picture and around Lake Maurepas is swampland.

Lakes Maurepas, Pontchartrain and Salvador, as well as others visible on the lower right-hand side of the image, are shallow and carry heavy sediment, which is what gives them their lighter green tones on the image. The causeway across Lake Pontchartrain stands out as a long white line that runs across to the lower edge of central New Orleans. The city dates from the early eighteenth century and is now the home of 600,000 people. The old city shows as a deeper blue-grey patch tucked into a bend in the river. The fine-grained criss-cross pattern of the main streets is visible within it. Below New Orleans, where the river is closest to Lake Pontchartrain, the Bonnet-Carré Floodway shows as a thin pink strip joining river and lake, with the black and white lines of a canal and service road running along each side. It was built in 1927, after a disastrous flood to New Orleans was averted only by destruction of other river levees, and it carries overflow water from the Mississippi to the lake.

The other sizeable city on this image, Baton Rouge, can be seen as a bluish patch at the lower left corner, on the bank of the Mississippi River. To the right of it is the Intracoastal Waterway. Part of it is visible running down the top right of the image, and another section is prominent as a blue-white line crossing the lower right of the image to Lake Palourde and the Atchfalaya River. The latter was once an independent stream, but it now connects to the Mississippi north of here and carries a quarter of that river's total discharge down to the Gulf of Mexico. The Grand River follows roughly the same course as the Intracoastal Waterway at the bottom of the image, but loops away from it to the north as a much thinner line. The Waterway is part of a large interconnected system of canals and rivers, covering much of eastern U.S.A.

Image scale and date: 1 cm = 4.3 km, October 1972.

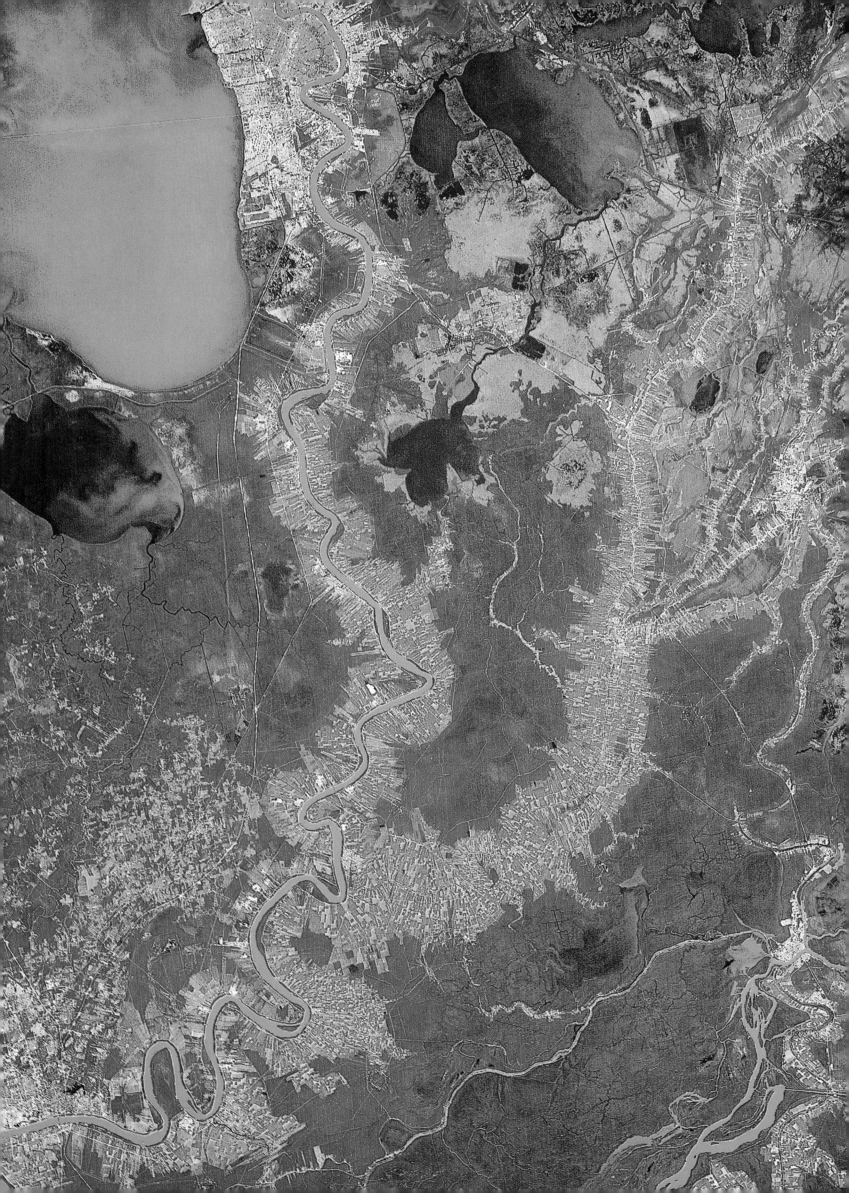

The Ubolratna Dam, Thailand

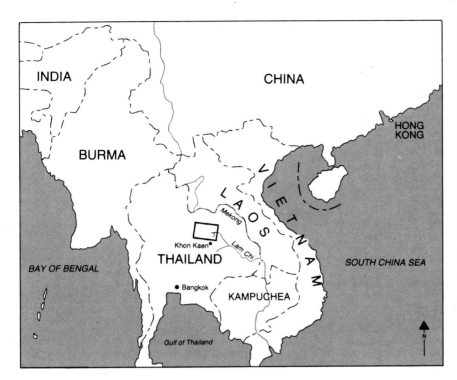

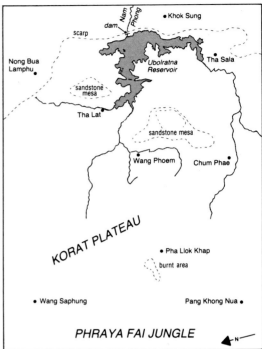

The area of Thailand displayed in this image is in the north-east part of the country. The border with Laos follows the winding course of the Mekong River, and lies about 160 kilometres (100 miles) away to the north and east. This whole image area falls in the Mekong watershed, and general river flows are from west to east.

The Ubolratna Dam and the Ubolratna, or Nam Phong, Reservoir seen in the upper part of the picture are one of Thailand's older hydro-electric projects. The nearest town of significance is Khon Kaen, about 24 kilometres (15 miles) south and just off the image. Commissioned by the Electricity Generating Authority of Thailand and completed in 1966, the Ubolratna Dam controls the irrigation for a large area to the east, and also provides a 25 megawatt hydro-electric power station with transmission lines running 400 kilometres (250 miles) south-west to the capital, Bangkok. Ubolratna is a good deal smaller than the better known Siri Kit and Bhumiphol Dams in the west of Thailand, which are newer and have several hundred megawatt capacity. All three dams are named after members of the current Thai royal family; in the case of Ubolratna, after the eldest princess.

The dark red vegetated scarp running along the top of the image and reservoir provides one of this scene's most striking features. The image was recorded at 9.30 a.m. in mid-January. The sun is low in the east. The shadows on the western side of the scarp and of the vegetated red mesas below it make it clear that the land to the east of the reservoir must be considerably higher than the reservoir itself. Thus the Nam Phong running off the top of the image appears to be flowing uphill as it moves east to its confluence with the Mekong. In fact, the river has over the millennia carved its own gorge through the steep scarp line.

This whole area forms part of the Korat Plateau of eastern Thailand, and the red-displayed vegetated mesas are sandstone, harder than the blue-white shales that surround them and covered with natural forest and scrub. Erosion has slowly lowered the level of the lighter-coloured areas, until the sandstones stand out as steep-sided mesas hundreds of metres above the floodplain. The same erosion process has scooped out the central part of some of the mesas, leaving depressions that show as light areas. Toward the bottom of the scene the greener patch on the central mesa is the result of a fire. Slash-and-burn agriculture is common here, and the regional government also uses burns to clear large areas before more systematic agricultural development. The blue-white parts of this image will show red with paddy rice, maize, and *kenaf* (a type of jute) later in the year. Tributaries leading to the reservoir are lined with irrigated agricultural land, already showing as narrow red lines on the image. Elsewhere the red areas are all jungle.

It is one of the objectives of the area's irrigation projects to permit more widespread multiple cropping, rather than the limited agriculture possible with 'rain-fed' crop production. The monsoon in this area provides heavy rainfall from July to September only. With the irrigation that the Nam Phong Reservoir provides, improved winter crops of mung beans, maize, and cassava can raise the subsistence-level farming of the region until it becomes a food exporter.

Image scale and date: 1 cm = 4.5 km, January 1976.

Israel and the Gaza Strip

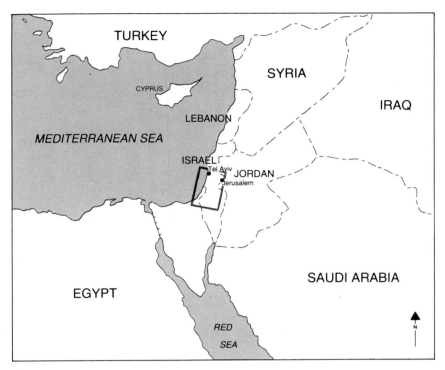

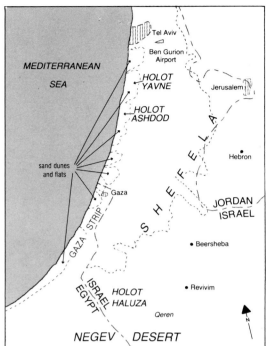

This scene covers the southern part of Israel from Tel Aviv in the north to the boundary with Egypt in the south. The image area corresponds to the Biblical regions of Samaria in the north, Judaea in the central part, and Idumea (Edom) in the south. Philistia lies to the south-west, in the area now known as the Gaza Strip.

Since the creation of the state of Israel in 1948, its people have systematically applied terracing, modern agricultural methods and irrigation to transform the land. The productive acreage has increased from about 160,000 hectares (400,000 acres) in 1948, to well over 400,000 hectares (1,000,000 acres) today, of which almost half is irrigated. All the productive land in this scene lies in Israel. The principal crops are barley, wheat, olives, grapes, cotton and citrus fruits. One can draw approximate national borders on the image, simply by delineating the areas where the red-displayed vegetation is at its brightest. The border with Egypt is particularly noticeable in the south, where the first steps have been taken by Israel to condition the dry land of the Negev Desert. A pipeline now carries fresh water from the Sea of Galilee in the north (off the image area) to the Negev, and the darker grey colour of the desert in Israel indicates the beginning of agriculture, extensive rather than intensive, contrasting with the unproductive Egyptian lands.

Tel Aviv, a city of a little over 1 million people, is visible as a large dark-grey patch on the Mediterranean coast in the upper part of the scene. The Ben Gurion Airport shows clearly to the east, as a white triangular pattern of runways. Moving south along the coast, the desert dunes of the Holot Yavne, Holot Ashdod, and other sandy tracts appear as bright patches of white. The city of Gaza lies at the northern end of the Gaza Strip, a patch of darker grey in the bright sand. Gaza was the great trade centre of ancient Philistia, a thriving city by 1500 B.C., famous for its light textiles (the word 'gauze' is taken from it).

Inland from the coastal plain lie the pinkish-grey foothills of Shefela, east of which the land rises to about 1,000 metres (3,300 feet) around Jerusalem and Hebron. Further east the land slopes down again to the Jordan Rift Valley, with its low point 400 metres (1,300 feet) below sea-level at the Dead Sea, 27 kilometres (17 miles) east of Hebron and beyond the right-hand edge of the image.

Jerusalem can be seen as a dark-grey patch in the hills on the upper right of the image. The ancient town of Beersheba, the Biblical southern limit of Palestine, is visible as a small blue-grey patch on the edge of the Negev Desert, almost due south of Tel Aviv.

Image scale and date: 1 cm = 4.8 km, January 1973.

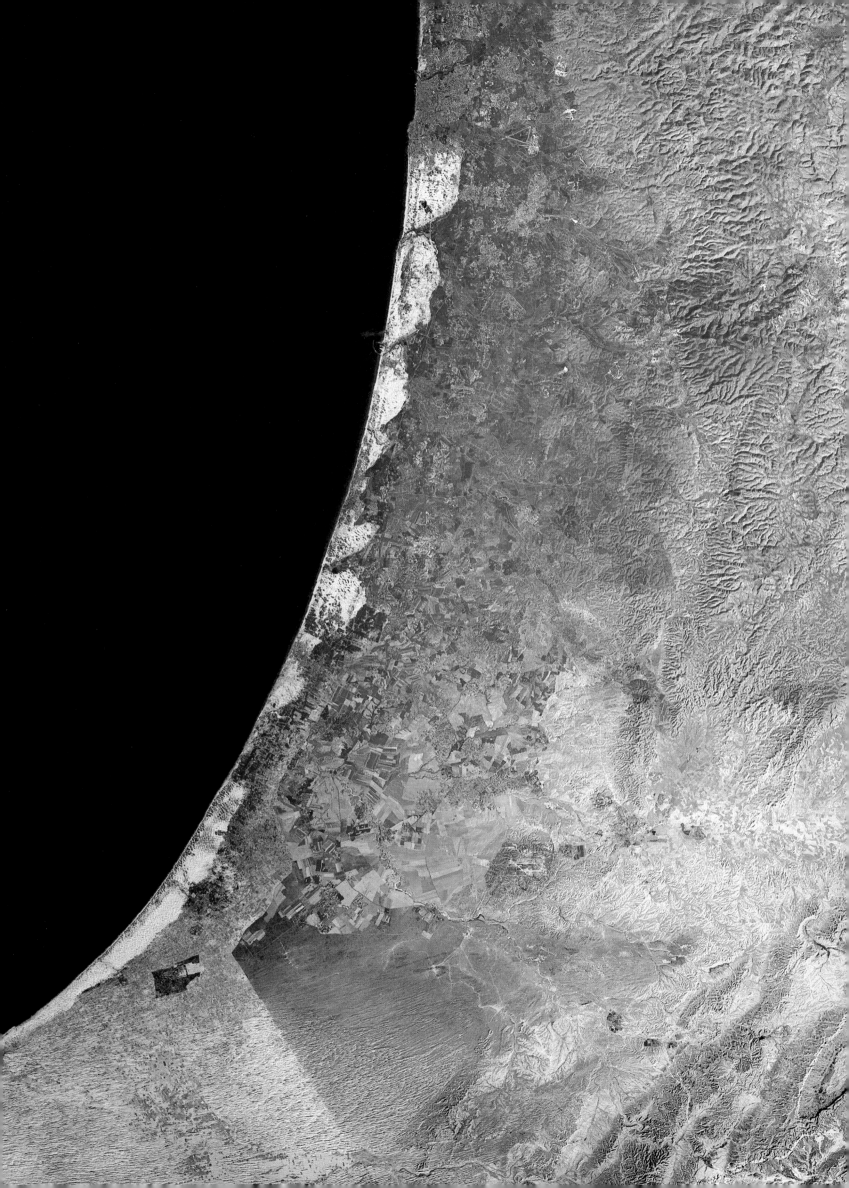

La Grande Hydro-electric Complex, Quebec

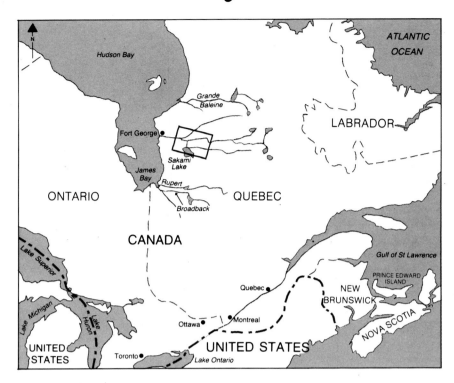

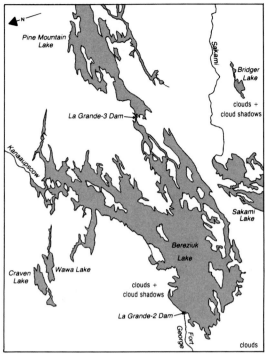

East of Canada's James Bay, stretching hundreds of kilometres across the province of Quebec, one of the world's largest hydro-electric projects is now taking shape. This image shows the central region of La Grande Complex, the series of dams, dykes and reservoirs that will by 1990 provide more than 10,000 megawatts of power to Ontario, Quebec, and the north-eastern U.S.A.

The numerous lakes visible in the scene were formed during the last Ice Age, when glaciers on their march south carved out deep ravines in the 600-million-year-old rocks of the Canadian Shield. Between the black lakes grows the taiga, subarctic evergreen forests of black spruce and jack pine seen as orange-red on the image. Many of the green and grey-green areas within the taiga are recent burns, slowly regrowing their forest cover. The type of terrain pictured on this scene extends over much of northern Canada, the degree of vegetative cover decreasing as one proceeds further north.

La Grande-2 dam is visible at the western end of Lake Bereziuk, at the bottom of the image. It shows as a greenish-white obstacle across the Fort George River, which further west becomes the La Grande River and flows into James Bay, 130 kilometres (80 miles) away. La Grande-2 was completed in 1981, and on this image its reservoir of Lake Bereziuk is still filling. The dam has sixteen turbines and will generate 5,300 megawatts of electricity (for comparison, Niagara Falls produces little more than half this amount, about 3,600 megawatts).

La Grande-3 is under development at the upper centre of the image. The construction work, with its network of service roads running in all directions, shows as a large green-white scar at the western end of Pine Mountain Lake. The dam is scheduled for completion in 1984, and its twelve turbines will produce 2,300 megawatts.

A series of additional dams will be built by Hydro-Quebec (formerly the James Bay Energy Company) during the 1980s, to yield a single 15,000-million-dollar water management system that extends well beyond the boundaries of this scene, and includes the watersheds of the La Grande River, the Grande Baleine River to the north, and the Nottaway-Rupert-Broadback river systems to the south. Bridger Lake, Craven Lake and the other small lakes visible on this image will be absorbed into the greatly expanded Sakami and Bereziuk Lakes, and the Sakami and Kanaaupscow Rivers will broaden to fill their present river valleys.

This part of Canada is the traditional home of Eskimos and of the Cree Indians. Under a 1975 agreement with the Government of Quebec the displaced inhabitants will receive a 13,000-square-kilometre (5,000-square-mile) native land reserve, and retain exclusive hunting, fishing, and trapping rights to 155,000 square kilometres (60,000 square miles) of land around the new reservoirs.

Image scale and date: 1 cm = 5.5 km, July 1981.

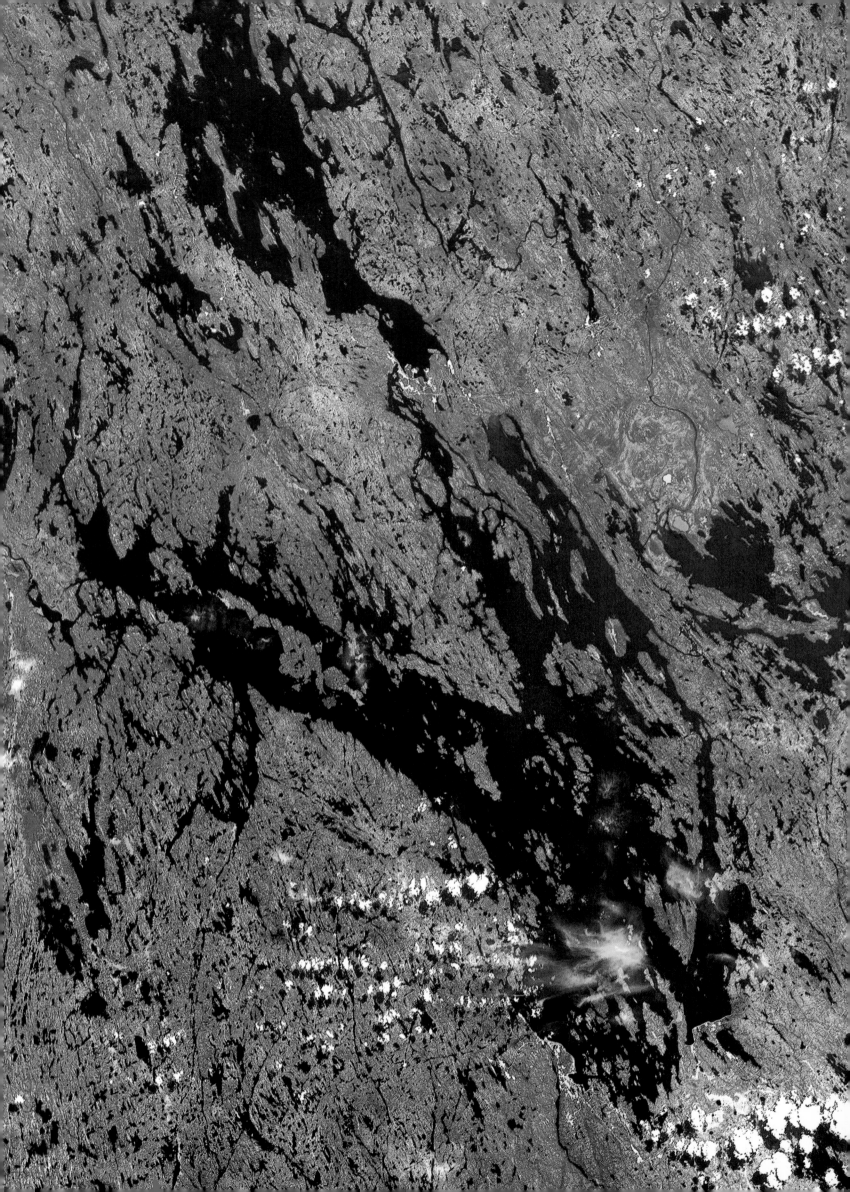

The Aswan High Dam, Egypt

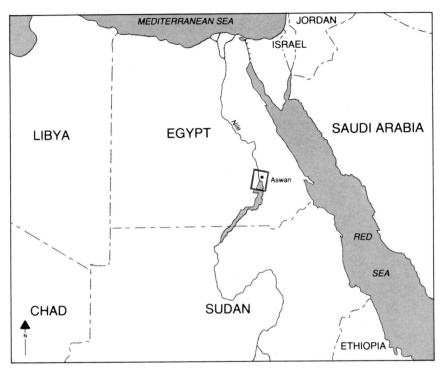

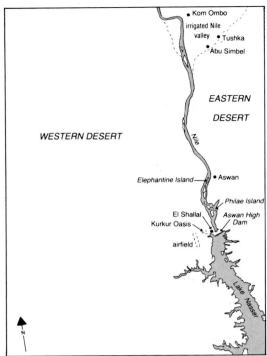

For more than 6,000 years the agriculture along the Egyptian Nile valley depended totally on the annual flooding of the river. With negligible local rainfall, all food production was the result of irrigation, but even so, without control of the river level there could be only one crop per year, and it was of variable quantity. River control, through a dam and reservoir, would permit perennial irrigation, and hence two to three crops each year. To accomplish this the Aswan High Dam was constructed, and it is shown here less than two years after its completion. The Nile is now completely controlled from Aswan to the Mediterranean.

The Aswan High Dam is not the first at this location, 690 kilometres (430 miles) south of Cairo. In 1902 a dam was built here which was heightened in 1912 and again in 1933. Finally, in 1960, work began on the present structure. Built by Egyptian workmen under Soviet supervision and located at the first cataract of the Nile, this dam is 111 metres (365 feet) high, more than 3 kilometres long, has 180 sluices, and holds back 130,000 million tonnes of water. It was completed in 1971. The resulting lake stretches south into Sudan, past the second cataract of the Nile. Within Egypt it is known as Lake Nasser, and within Sudan it is Lake Nuba.

The grey bar of the dam as it sits astride the Nile is easily seen on this image, with the spreading lake to the south and the irrigated river valley to the north.

The dam is just up-river of Aswan, at El Shallal, and the airfield at El Shallal is seen as a grey vertical stripe just west of the dam. The image area extends from the palaeolithic site of Kom Ombo in the north, where the ascending black thread of the Nile kinks sharply to the west, on down past the red irrigated area of Tushka and Abu Simbel east of the river. The southern image boundary falls 50 kilometres (30 miles) north of the limit of the Egyptian Empire under the Ptolemies. The lake and river stand out starkly against the arid tans and dark greys of the desert, in which blown sand west of the Nile creates brilliant buff streaks against the sombre background of dry rock.

The whole area contains developments of great antiquity. Aswan itself, under its old names of Swan, Syene, and Seveneh, is mentioned often in ancient writings, including the prophecies of Ezekiel. When the High Dam was built, many historic sites were destroyed and others relocated. Several are found now on the western bank just south of the dam, including the Beit el Wali built by Rameses II, the unique Roman temple known as the Kiosk of Qertassi, and the Kalabsha erected by Augustus Caesar. Other antiquities have been relocated to Elephantine Island which is visible in the Nile, as is the ancient site of Philae Island, a few kilometres north of the Aswan High Dam.

Image scale and date: 1 cm = 2.9 km, November 1972.

Commerce and Trade

Money is a relatively recent human invention, introduced about 550 B.C. by the Lydians of Asia Minor. The origins of barter, commerce and trade are far older, lost in pre-history, but it was these activities that largely created and built today's great cities.

The cities originally served two primary purposes, each with quite different requirements. As a focal point for defence of a region, a city had to have a non-interruptible water supply and be easily defended, either by walls or an inaccessible natural setting. On the other hand, to develop an effective trading centre for food and goods, ease of access by land and sea was essential, along with certain other requirements. Concentrating on the needs of commerce (though to many of the ancient capitals defence needs held the higher priority), we can list the factors that over the centuries have stimulated the growth of a city at a particular location: the site should lie at the centre of a fertile agricultural plain or close to productive mineral mines, in order to provide a source of materials for trade; the site should be well provided with fresh water; there should be easy land transportation routes to other major centres of either supply or demand; there should be an easy water transportation route, open year-round, for shipment abroad of very heavy materials; and the site should enjoy an equable climate, permitting year-round operation of trade facilities.

It is instructive to examine the images that follow and see how well the world's trade centres match this list of desirable features. Every city has excellent access by water: they lie on the coast, or on a major navigable river, or (in the case of Chicago) on a great lake. All have good land transportation routes to other major markets and urban centres, although in the case of Sydney the distances involved are great and sea transport is preferred. And all have a climate that allows commercial operations to be conducted all the year round. It is only when we look at water supplies, food supplies, and surrounding agriculture that anomalies appear and point to the changing nature of world commerce.

San Diego lies in a near-desert but is one of the world's fastest-growing commercial areas. Since water today can be brought from great distances at acceptable cost, the city's fine harbour and excellent climate more than compensate for the dryness. Perhaps more important, it specializes in handling high-technology products, which depend more on careful handling than on very high port capacity. Similarly, Cape Town is in a moderately productive area, but the true reason for its success as a port lies as much in the high-value, low-weight commodities of gold, platinum, and diamonds that are shipped from there as in the city's splendid harbour.

This is the pattern of the future. By the end of the century, many of the new great centres of commerce will lack the familiar land and sea routes, the abundant water supply, and easy all-season access. Instead, commerce will be centred where the high-value, low-weight products are made — electronics, optics, computer circuits, aircraft instruments, medical equipment, and communications equipment. Because the products are small and light they can be shipped economically by land, sea, or air all over the world. Just as the industrial revolution caused the rapid rise of a whole new group of cities, in twenty years a new set of trading cities will be the nodes for global commerce.

New York

 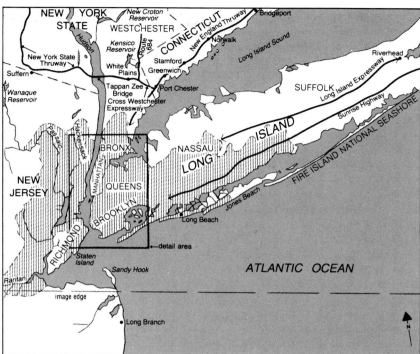

New York City is the world's busiest financial centre and America's most active port and biggest city. Many of the most famous features of the city are visible on the summer image reproduced overleaf.

Central Park shows as a red oblong in the middle of Manhattan Island, with the Central Park Reservoir clearly visible as a dark area at its centre. On the west side of Manhattan the city's wharves and jetties make a fine sawtooth pattern jutting into the Hudson River, and other major docking facilities are visible across the river in New Jersey. On the east side the Brooklyn Bridge, Manhattan Bridge, and Williamsburg Bridge connect Manhattan and Brooklyn boroughs across the East River. To the south lies Governors Island, now federal property, and closer to the shore of New Jersey are the much smaller Ellis Island, the arrival point for most American immigrants earlier this century, and Liberty Island, whose Statue of Liberty provides the most spectacular feature of upper New York Bay.

South of Manhattan lie Staten Island and the Borough of Richmond, the only one of New York's five boroughs that still shows significant amounts of red-displayed vegetation. The Verrazano-Narrows Bridge to Brooklyn, with its 1,298-metre (4,260-foot) main span, is clearly visible north-east of Staten Island. Out to the east on Long Island, Kennedy Airport can just be perceived as a blue-white pattern of runways north of Jamaica Bay. The blue tones representing the airport's asphalt and buildings compete with the blue surrounding urban areas, making it difficult to separate the two types of land

use. Further along the southern shore are the resort areas of Rockaway Beach, Long Beach, and Jones Beach, and the long public front of Fire Island. The causeway connecting Jones Beach to the mainland is visible as a light north-south line. The Long Island Expressway running out to Riverhead shows up clearly on the eastern end of the island, with Sunrise Highway parallel to and south of it.

North of Manhattan Island lies the Borough of the Bronx, and beyond that Westchester County and upper New York State. The Cross Westchester Expressway is visible as a green-white line as it runs through White Plains and then goes on west to merge with the New York State Thruway as it heads across the Hudson River on the Tappan Zee Bridge, and away through Suffern to the north-west. East of White Plains, Route 684 stands out clearly as it runs past Kensico Reservoir to join Route 84 at Brewster, just off the top of the image. North of Long Island Sound, in the upper part of the image, the New England Thruway is visible as it threads its way through the Connecticut towns of Greenwich, Stamford, Norwalk, and Bridgeport, visible as blue-grey patches against their more vegetated surroundings.

West of New York lie the New Jersey commuter suburbs, accessible from Manhattan by tunnels under the Hudson River and by the George Washington Bridge, visible at the upper end of Manhattan Island. With the Connecticut, Long Island, and New Jersey suburbs, more than 13 million people live and work within 50 kilometres (30 miles) of New York City.

Image scale and date: 1 cm = 3.4 km, August 1976.

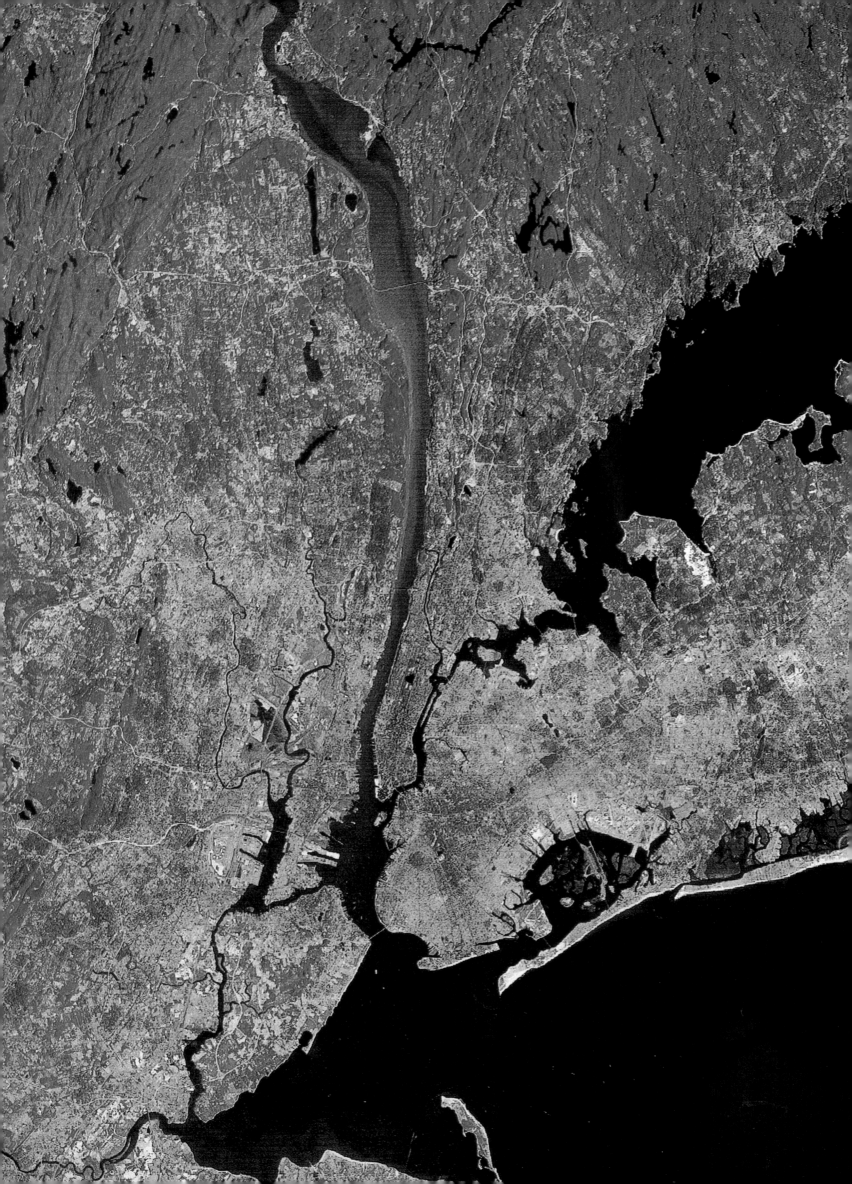

The Bristol Channel and South Wales

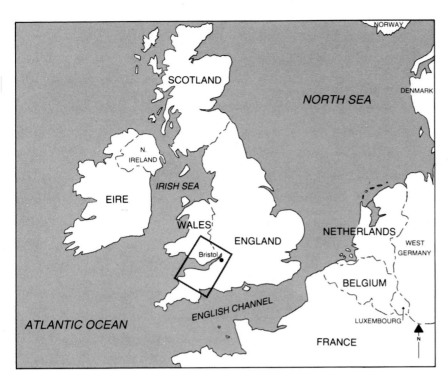

For hundreds of years Bristol was England's second-biggest city and seaport, the centre for shipbuilding and a major centre for trade, particularly the slave trade, inferior only to London in size and volume of traffic. Standing on the east bank of the wide estuary of the Bristol Channel, the city is seen here as a grey-green patch at the right centre of this winter image. With a population of 450,000, Bristol and its associated port of Avonmouth form the major centre of west England commerce.

The broad blue-green swath of the Bristol Channel occupies the centre of the scene. Streaks and swirls within the channel indicate that it is highly sedimented, but it is deep enough to permit large ocean-going ships, up to 14 metre (46 feet) draft, to use the docks at Avonmouth. The channel narrows abruptly between Bristol and Gloucester, to become the meandering River Severn.

Most major towns of the region are readily visible on this image as blue-grey patches against red-displayed vegetation. On the south shore of the Bristol Channel are Weston super Mare, Minehead (partly hidden by broken cloud), and Ilfracombe, with Barnstaple and Bideford visible inland from Barnstaple Bay. On the northern side of the channel, the River Wye between Chepstow and Monmouth marks the border between England and Wales. It then snakes up through Hereford to the Elan Valley Reservoirs which supply Birmingham. The Severn Bridge at Chepstow shows as a faint dark-blue line.

The contrast between the economic life of the areas above and below the channel is clearly visible. Centuries of agricultural exploitation have produced the light-red mottled colouring of south-west England and the coastal strip of Wales. Just above Cardiff the much more recent economic explosion of the Industrial Revolution has left its mark in the grey-green urban sprawl filling the valleys from Merthyr Tydfil and Ebbw Vale down as far as Caerphilly. Roads and railways run down all the valleys, converging on Cardiff and Newport which are ideally situated to handle the iron and coal exported from the area. Such a specialized economy is extremely vulnerable to change, and the exploitation of other sources of energy, such as gas, oil, hydro-electric and nuclear power, has led to high unemployment in the twentieth century. One of the results of the attempts of recent governments to solve this problem and attract new industry is the creation of the New Town of Cwmbran, just below Pontypool.

The M5 motorway can be seen as a continuous thin blue line that begins at Exeter, runs to the north passing east of Taunton and Bridgwater, then moves closer to the Severn River to skirt the Mendip Hills. It passes east of Weston super Mare and heads on to disappear into the urban mass of Bristol. North of that city the motorway again becomes visible, running on north up to Gloucester.

The rugged moors, hills and mountains in this scene are readily recognized by their lack of the light-red displayed vegetation visible elsewhere on the image and by their grey-green colour. South of the channel is Exmoor, a light-green mass of sandstone standing out from the agricultural lands around it. Further north, in Wales, the sandstones and limestones around Aberdare, and in the Black Mountains (peaks cloud-covered) and Cambrian Mountains are all seen as pale green, convoluted areas, with scattered patches of dark-red forest. The Brecon Beacons are visible just south-west of the Black Mountains, and in the top right of the image are the Malvern Hills.

Image scale and date: 1 cm = 5.7 km, February 1976.

Cape Town

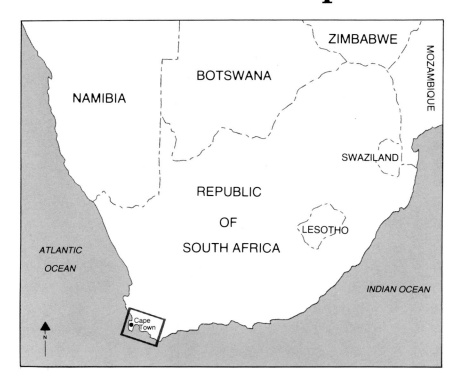

Main passenger and mail port for South Africa, seat of the country's parliament, and the world's leading export centre for gold and diamonds, Cape Town is a city of about 1 million people, situated at the northern end of the hooked peninsula that terminates in the Cape of Good Hope. Discovered by Bartholomew Diaz in 1486, the Cape forms the south-west tip of the continent of Africa.

Table Mountain, with its unique 1,066-metre (3,500-foot) flat top, shows as a red patch to the right of the blue-grey city, with the Twelve Apostles range adjoining it. The docks and harbours of Cape Town are built on reclaimed land at Heerengracht, on Table Bay, while the city itself has spread right across the narrow peninsula. Cape Town urban development can be seen as it runs east through the suburb of Bellville, and south as far as Muizenberg, whose bathing beaches on the shores of False Bay are reputed to be the finest in Africa. They show on this image as a thin white line along the shore. To the right of Muizenberg, Simonstown, a major naval base, dockyard and tidal basin, is just visible.

Cape Town and its suburbs receive moderate rainfall, but inland and to the north the climate rapidly becomes much drier. The land also rises steadily as we move north-east, and the rugged line of the Langeberg range at the upper left corner of the image forms the beginning of the high plateau that constitutes the inland portion of Cape Province. Between the coastal plain and the elevated plateau, around Paarl and Stellenbosch in the valley below the dark Drakenstein Mountains, the climate is well suited to viniculture. The production of wine and soft fruit in these areas provides one of Cape Town's significant exports (the K.W.V. wine cellars at Paarl are among the largest in the world). Further right the bright red patch of the Elgin Basin indicates another productive agricultural area, this one especially noted for apples and grains.

The principal wheat-growing area of Cape Province is visible on this scene as a fine-textured mottled pattern of green (harvested fields) and red (growing crops), bordered on the left by the Riviersonderend and covering much of the land area of the upper central part of the picture. The mountains to the left of the wheat belt have very little rainfall, and in the absence of masking vegetation the dark rocks stand out clearly.

The bottom left-hand part of the scene shows by its white and light-green colours that there is far less vegetation here than on the rest of the image area. By Melkbosstrand the rainfall is down to less than 25 centimetres (10 inches) a year, and the bare white landscape marks the beginning of a semi-desert that extends hundreds of kilometres north, to become the true desert of the Kalahari.

Image scale and date: 1 cm = 5.8 km, March 1981.

Hamburg

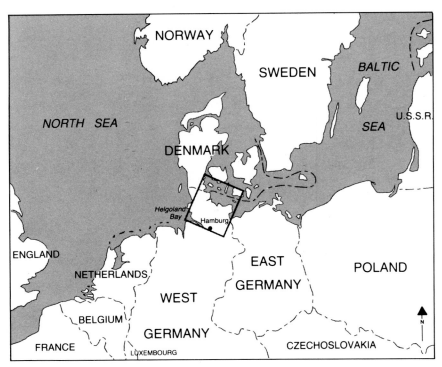 

Hamburg is West Germany's most important industrial town and Europe's greatest seaport. With a population of 1.25 million, it ranks in size second only to Berlin (population 2 million) in Germany.

The city is visible at the bottom of this image as a large, sprawling, blue-grey area amid red agricultural countryside. The River Elbe, second largest river in Germany, with its broad estuary opening to the North Sea at Helgoland Bay (just off the image to the west), can be seen on the left side of the picture with distinctive field patterns above and below it. At Hamburg the river divides into a complex pattern of docks and canals. In the northern part of the city the Fuhlsbüttel Airport shows as lighter blue lines of runway within the overall blue of urban development.

Hamburg lies at the southern edge of the West German *Land*, or province, of Schleswig-Holstein, whose north-west part, bordering on Denmark, was the subject of complex political dispute in the last century when both Germany and Denmark claimed it. The whole region is an important agricultural area, producing cereals, flax, cattle, and apples and other fruit. North of Hamburg, the isolated remaining patches of woodland, mainly spruce, stand out darker brownish-red amidst the planted fields. Blue areas that look as though they ought to be towns but are not marked on the map are cleared fields and groups of fields. (Small cleared fields can often be distinguished by their regular layout, but groups of fields are a much more difficult problem. The new wavelengths provided by the Landsat-4 spacecraft, which was launched in July 1982, will greatly ease the problem.)

The fine blue-grey line of the motorway north from Hamburg is visible as it runs up west of Neumünster and branches there north to Kiel and north-west through the towns of Rendsburg, Schleswig, and Flensburg, and on into Denmark. The 98-kilometre (61-mile) long Kiel Canal (Nord-Ostsee-Kanal), dug in 1895, can be traced as a black line on the image, from its southern end at Brunsbüttel on the Elbe estuary up through Rendsburg to the northern terminus at Kiel. The canal will pass ships up to 9 metre (30 foot) draft, and forms the shortest and quickest sea route from the North Sea to the Baltic.

Kiel is West Germany's largest Baltic port. The city dates back to A.D. 1250, but since it was almost completely destroyed by air raids in the Second World War it is structurally a post-war city. The great harbour, 11 kilometres (7 miles) long and 3 kilometres (nearly 2 miles) across at its mouth, is easily seen on this picture despite a light covering of cloud that extends east from Kiel to Lübeck Bay. Beyond Lübeck, agricultural patterns permit one to trace the boundary between East and West Germany. East of the border, the fields are much larger, and there are more cleared areas (light-blue on the image). In the west, agriculture is intense.

The water boundary between Denmark and Germany runs across the top of Kiel Bay. The islands at the top of the image thus all belong to Denmark, with the exception of West-German-controlled Fehmarn. The red dot just north-east of Kiel Harbour and the straight dark streak to the right of that are not physical features but a region of lost data from the satellite. The land boundary between Denmark and Germany runs just north of Flensburg. Below Flensburg, in the left centre of the image, the dark thread of the River Eider is visible running west towards the North Sea.

Image scale and date: 1 cm = 6 km, June 1978.

Montreal

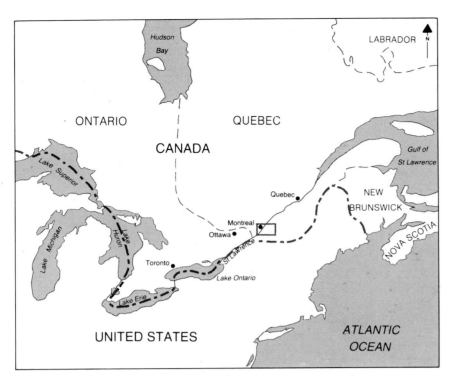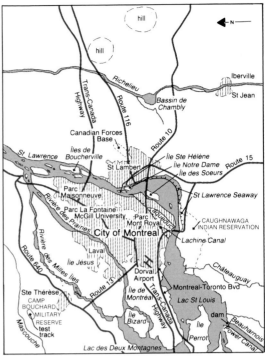

Canada's largest city and greatest eastern port, Montreal is built on a group of islands at the confluence of the Ottawa and St Lawrence Rivers. The St Lawrence River can be seen bisecting this image area. The United States border lies 30 kilometres (20 miles) to the south, and Ontario is 30 kilometres west. The principal islands around Montreal are all visible in this scene: Perrot at the bottom right; the small island of Bizard to the left; and the main ones, Île Jésus and Île de Montréal, dominating the picture. Most of Montreal's population of 2.8 million are found on Île de Montréal, the oldest and most heavily developed of the group.

This May image reveals the city and surrounding areas in remarkable detail. Within Montreal the parks of Mont Royal, La Fontaine, and Maisonneuve all stand out as bright red patches against the blue-grey urban development. Below Parc Mont Royal and the nearby campus of McGill University lie the runway patterns of Dorval Airport, used by Montreal for Canadian and U.S. flights. The international airport of Mirabel lies just off the bottom left-hand corner of the image. The dark lines of an aqueduct and the Lachine Canal are visible in the top right of the city.

At the top of Montreal, in the St Lawrence River beyond the extensive docks, lie two island parks: Île Ste Hélène, with the Lac des Dauphins and Port Ste Hélène visible at its left-hand end; and the Île Notre Dame, with the Lac des Régates a tiny black dot on the left tip of the island and the long pool of the Olympic Basin visible as a dark line. To their right is the Île des Soeurs, and further left in the river lie the Îles de Boucherville, with the bridge leading to the Trans-Canada Highway faintly visible at the right-hand end.

On the right of the St Lawrence, above Lac St Louis, the canal of the St Lawrence Seaway can be traced as a black line and then a faint white line along the top curve of the river. It provides a navigable waterway all the way from the Great Lakes to the Atlantic Ocean. To the right of it is the bright red area of the Caughnawaga Indian Reservation.

Many of the sixteen bridges that connect Montreal to the mainland are visible on this image, as well as several across the Rivière des Prairies between Montreal and Île Jésus and over the Rivière des Milles Îles to Ste Thérèse, lower left on the image. A few kilometres beyond Ste Thérèse, to the right of the Mascouche River, lies the dark red Camp Bouchard Military Reserve. Near the left-hand edge of the camp the Canadian Government's Auto Testing Laboratory and Track shows as a well-defined white oval.

The top part of the scene is mainly rural and shows French influence in the characteristic 'long lot' pattern of agriculture noted earlier in the Mississippi Delta. Within the pattern of fields the towns of St Jean and Iberville are visible on the Richelieu River. Left of them the narrow lines of Routes 10 and 116 and the Trans-Canada Highway (Route 20) are clearly visible. The Trans-Canada Highway proceeds to Montreal via the Îles de Boucherville, and after passing through the city heads west via the extreme bottom tip of Montreal Island. The bright red circular areas above the Richelieu River are relatively steep sloped hills, unfavourable for agriculture, which have been left in their native woodland state.

Image scale and date: 1 cm = 2.5 km, May 1978.

Rio de Janeiro

Largest harbour and chief port of Brazil, Rio de Janeiro was also the country's capital until the new city of Brasilia was constructed in 1960. This summer January image (Rio lies at 23 degrees south) displays the city's superb natural location for a deep-sea port.

The Baía de Guanabara, 26 kilometres (16 miles) long and 24 kilometres (15 miles) across, is protected from the Atlantic Ocean by the promontories of Sugar Loaf Mountain (Pão de Açúcar) in the west and the Parrot's Beak (Pico do Papagaio) in the east. The bay is deep enough to admit the largest vessels. Rio de Janeiro, a city of nearly 5 million people, occupies the alluvial plain on the west side of the Baía de Guanabara. It stretches down almost as far as Campo Grande and is separated from the famous beaches that lie along the Atlantic coast by the Corcovado's 700-metre (2,300-foot) ridge (displayed red on this image). Leme, Copacabana, Ipanema, Leblon and Gavea beaches extend from Sugar Loaf Mountain all the way down to the Tijuca sandbar.

Within the Baía de Guanabara, Rio's international Galeão Airport is just visible on the lower side of the bay's largest island, Ilha do Governador. Near the smaller island of Ilha da Cidade Universitária the long line of the Rio Niterói Bridge can be seen connecting Rio de Janeiro with the residential city of Niterói on the opposite shore. At the top end of the bay the urban development gives way to the dark brownish-reds and greens of low-lying swampland, while lower down to the left the land steadily rises and becomes part of the Serra dos Orgãos mountain range. The Serra dos Orgãos National Park shows as a fine spider-web pattern of green distinct from the natural mountain vegetation.

The lower half of this image is more rural and less densely populated. The sandbars and national park of Tijuca continue down from the beaches of Rio past the red ridge of the Serra do Bangú and extend into the long line of the Restinga de Marambaía, the spit that shelters the Baía de Sepetiba. The pale-blue areas on the upper left shore of the bay are lagoon areas, the top one with a red vegetated barrier to the right of it. To the north-east, in the centre of the image, the white patch is an empty lake with a red island of vegetation in its centre. Twenty-four kilometres (15 miles) north of the bay, beyond the red-displayed evergreen forest of the Serra Itaguçu, the dark outline of the Ribeirão das Lajes Reservoir is clearly visible. Hydro-electric power generated there is transmitted down to Volta Redonda, where iron ore shipped from Minas Gerais north of the image area is made into steel. Volta Redonda shows as an extended blue-grey patch in the bottom left of the picture. The finished steel is exported from the north shore ports of the Baía de Sepetiba.

The blue line of the Paraíba River separates the Serra do Couto from the higher Serra da Mantiqueira. The edge of the latter is visible in the bottom left-hand corner of the image; its highest point, north-west of the image area, is nearly 2,800 metres (9,200 feet). It is part of an elevated inland region that continues all the way to Brasilia, 800 kilometres (500 miles) away to the north-west.

Image scale and date: 1 cm = 4.2 km, January 1978.

Chicago

Chicago is the second largest city of the United States, and the transportation, industrial, and commercial centre of the north central region. Built on terrain formerly occupied by an ancient expansive lake, Chicago is located south-west of the present Lake Michigan. It is the home of 7 million people, and the city and its suburbs appear as a wide blue-grey sprawl across this autumn image.

The business centre of Chicago is the Chicago Loop, the darker area seen here just to the left of the white strip of Meigs Field airport. Beside it the Navy Pier is visible, jutting 900 metres (3,000 feet) into Lake Michigan, and beyond it shows the red line of Belmont Harbor Park and the downturned fishhook of Montrose-Wilson Beach. To the right of Meigs Field the campus of the University of Chicago can be seen as a thin red vertical line, above the larger red rectangle of Washington Park.

The border between Illinois and Indiana is further right along the lake shore, running along the top of the dark blue of Wolf Lake at Calumet Harbor. The blue patch below Wolf Lake is Lake Calumet. Further along the lake shore to the right lies the town of Gary, Indiana, the home of U.S. Steel's largest plant and the area's leading centre for steel production. Eleven kilometres (7 miles) of lake front are owned by the company, and the industrial development and slag dumps there show as a marked blue-white patch.

Above Gary on the image, extending to Michigan City and the Michigan border, the faint white line of the famous Indiana Dunes can be seen, now a protected area of lake shore and a state park.

As the hub of north central American industry, Chicago is well served by roads, railways, canals and airports. The Midway Airport is visible as a white-speckled red square criss-crossed by runways, straight down from Washington Park and to the right of the Chicago Ship Canal. O'Hare Airport, the world's busiest, lies to the left of the city, close to the heavily vegetated left to right red line of the Des Plaines River. The two dark lines of the Des Plaines River and the Chicago Ship Canal are met lower down by the end of the Calumet Sag Channel before continuing down to Joliet and beyond, to meet the Illinois River. The Illinois and Michigan Canal also runs from the centre of the city to Joliet, but it is not visible as a separate waterway on the image.

The right-hand side of the image is an intensively cultivated patchwork of fields, with corn, wheat, soya beans and oats the main crops. Cattle provide a major industry, and Chicago remains the country's centre for meat processing. The network of major roads that carries these products to and from Chicago is clearly visible as numerous fine white lines across the image (see map for identification). The black patch centre right on the picture is Cedar Lake.

Image scale and date: 1 cm = 4.9 km, October 1975.

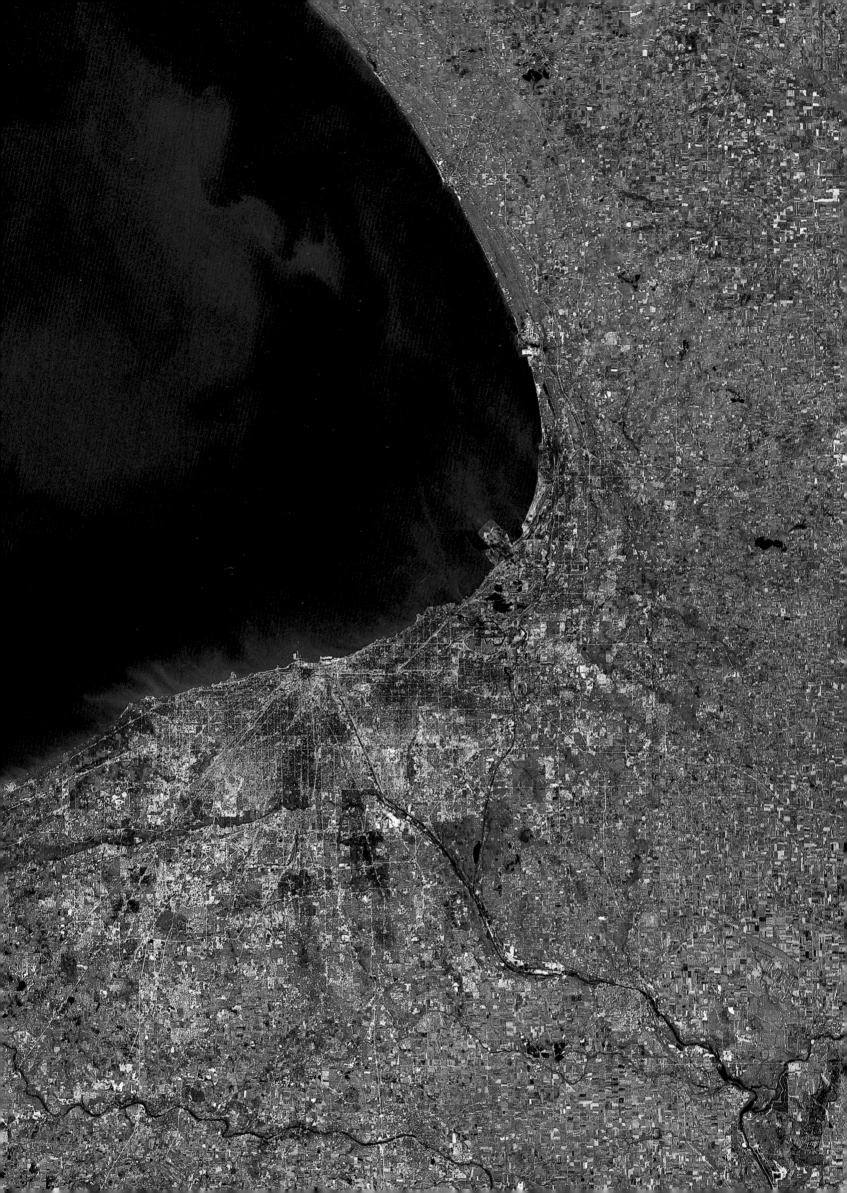

Naples

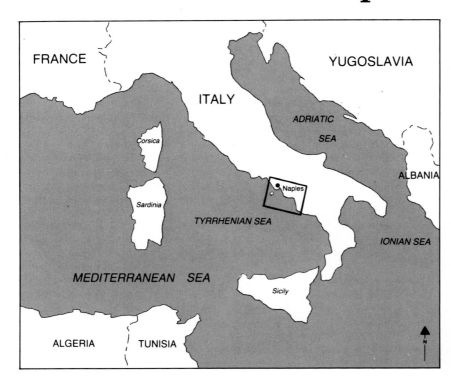

Neapolis to the Romans, it was a favourite home for emperors; Nero spent a lot of time here, and so did Hadrian and Marcus Aurelius. In the Middle Ages it was the capital of the 'Kingdom of the Two Sicilies'; until the beginning of this century it was the country's biggest city. Today Naples is one of Italy's chief industrial centres, its third largest city (after Rome and Milan), and a seaport second only to Genoa.

Seen here as a blue area of intense urban development, the city stands on the north side of the Golfo di Napoli. Its extensive docks and harbours are clearly visible in the gulf, with the blue line of the 1.5 kilometre-long Molo San Vincenzo jetty running out from the western shore. The whole coastal plain shows blue-grey on this image, in marked contrast to the bright red of the vegetated volcanic hills.

The Capo di Posillipo, with the tiny island of Nisida visible at its lower tip, divides the Golfo di Napoli from the Golfo di Baiae. Beyond Baiae the coast curves down to Monte di Procida, and a few kilometres offshore in the Tyrrhenian Sea stands the island of Procida, with the larger island of Ischia further out. The crater of the 790-metre (2,600-foot) Monte Epomeo ('Lookout Mountain') shows as a red circle in the centre of Ischia. Although the volcano is regarded as extinct, the presence of hot springs and earthquakes in the last century shows that the area is still seismically very active. On the mainland, to the left of

Monte di Procida, the coastline is marked by numerous lagoons as far as the Volturno River at the bottom left of the image. These swampy lagoons are now being slowly drained and cultivated.

More striking evidence of volcanic activity can be seen above Naples. The dark-green cone of Mount Vesuvius (1,277-metres; 4,190 feet) stands out clearly against the lush lava-fertilized vegetation clothing its lower slopes. Pompeii is just above and to the right of it, and Herculaneum is just below and to the right. Both Roman cities were buried by the famous eruption of A.D. 79. Castellammare di Stabia, also caught in the same volcanic outburst, is a well-known shipbuilding centre visible at the top of the Golfo di Napoli. The last major eruption of Vesuvius was in 1906, when the outline of the cone was modified to its present shape, but the volcano is far from quiet.

Beyond Vesuvius lies the long Sorrento Peninsula, with the tourist and resort island of Capri visible off its tip. Amalfi lies on the far shore of the peninsula, with Salerno visible as a bright blue strip further up the image at the northern end of the Golfo di Salerno. The red ridge of the Monti Lattari runs along the peninsula from Punta Campanella to join the Monti Picentini and beyond them the Neapolitan Apennines which are off the edge of the image. The scene area continues up as far as Agrapoli, Castellabate, and the unvegetated point of Punta Licosa.

Image scale and date: 1 cm = 4.1 km, July 1981.

San Diego

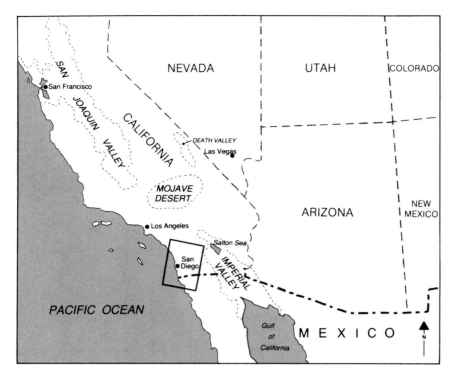

The climate in the south-west United States is pleasant, mild, and equable. Given an adequate supply of imported water (the natural rainfall is less than 25 centimetres a year) the area should be ideal for both agriculture and industry. San Diego, which since 1950 has experienced a population growth from 0.5 million to 1.5 million, provides an excellent example of this point. It is the home for an increasing fraction of the U.S. aerospace programme, and enjoys a booming agricultural export trade. It serves as the first U.S. entry point for vessels passing through the Panama Canal, and also as the natural port for the Imperial Valley, the prodigiously productive agricultural area that lies south of the Salton Sea, east of this image.

The city lies on a fine natural harbour only 16 kilometres (10 miles) from the Mexican border. San Diego Bay shows as a long inlet of the Pacific Ocean, shielded from bad weather by a curving line of dunes that terminate to the north at the blue-grey city of Coronado and the white runways of the North Island Naval Air Station.

To the east, within the blue-grey city of San Diego, Balboa Park with its famous zoo and recreation areas is readily seen as a red and white square. South of it, on the east shore of the bay, the wharves and jetties are blue comb-teeth projecting into the water. The thin blue line of the bridge to Coronado is visible below the narrow northern neck of the bay, while at its southern end, drying sand ponds are revealed as a faint pattern of lines within the water off Imperial Beach.

The whole area is a centre for U.S. Navy activities. West of Coronado, on the long south-facing Point Loma peninsula, lies a U.S. Naval Reservation. On the mainland, between the Naval Reservation and the city of San Diego, the white runways of the international civilian airport of Lindbergh Field can be seen. At the north end of Point Loma peninsula, beyond the town of Ocean Beach, the floodway for the San Diego River shows as a dark horizontal line, and just above it is Mission Beach and the dark ponds and inlets of Mission Bay Park. Beyond that, on a jutting point of land, is La Jolla, home of the Scripps Institute of Oceanography. A number of dark lagoons, crossed by the blue line of Route 101 to Los Angeles, breach the shoreline further north.

East of Route 101 the town of Escondido and the light-red Santa Maria Valley to the south-east of it are fertile centres for citrus and avocado production. North-east of Escondido, close to the boundary of the scene, the grass-covered Warner Basin shows a lighter pink with Lake Henshaw at its left-hand end. Most of this area of the image forms part of the uncultivated Santa Ysabel Indian Reservation, with the browner and less vegetated upper right corner marking the beginning of the true inland desert.

Near the southern edge of the scene, the Mexican border is clearly visible from the abrupt change in the amount of vegetation. North of the border the land is bright red, irrigated and productive; to the south it is dry, brownish-white and bare. The Mexican town of Tijuana shows as a blue patch right at the border.

Image scale and date: 1 cm = 3.3 km, February 1977.

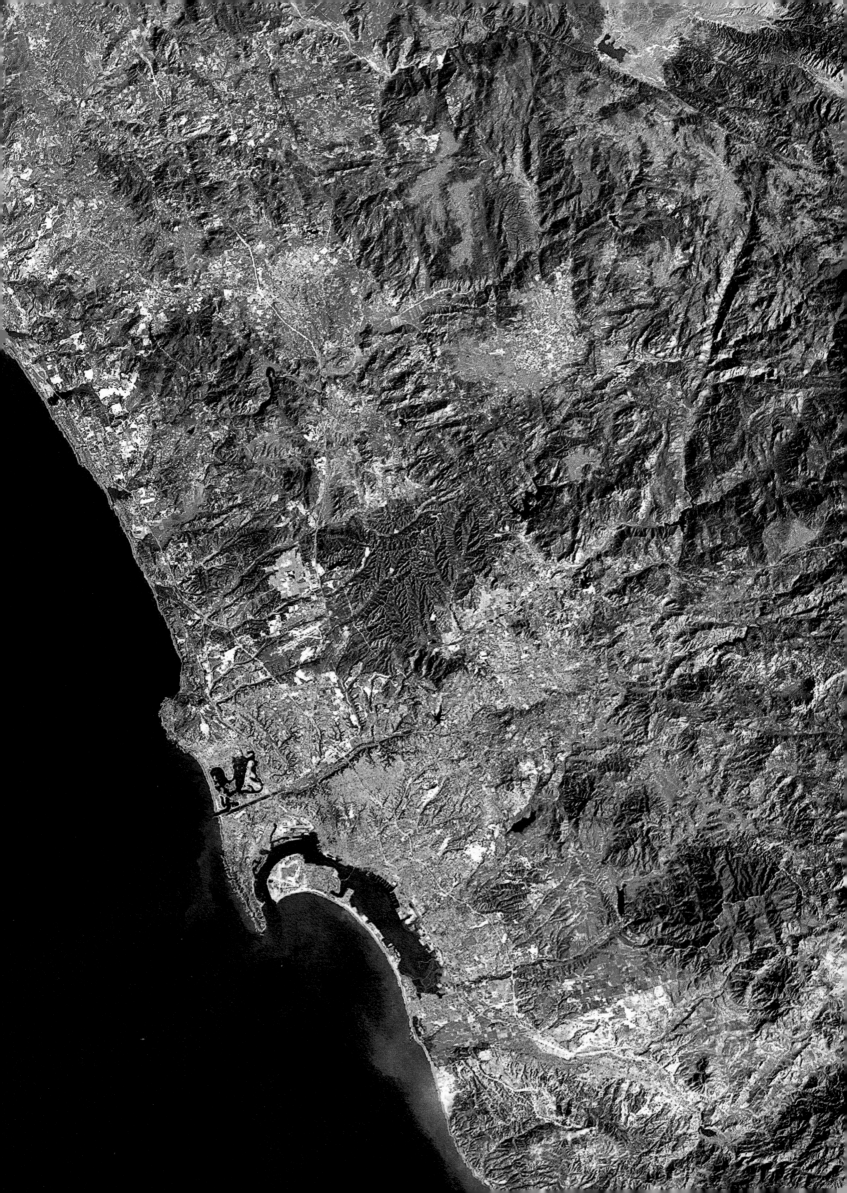

Sydney

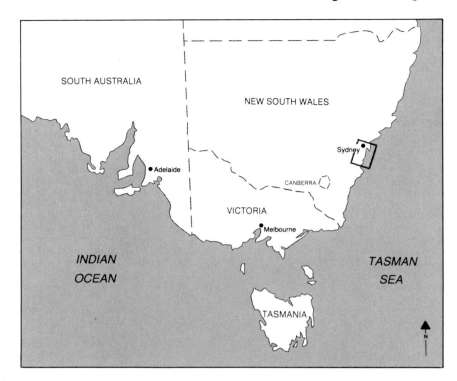

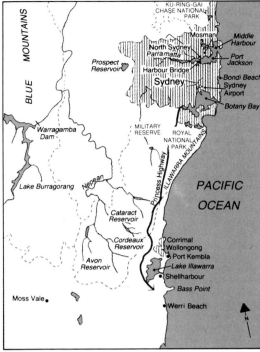

More than one-fifth of the population of Australia lives in the blue-grey area near the top of this image. Sydney, with almost 3 million inhabitants, is the continent's biggest city and leading port. It is also the capital of the state of New South Wales. The coastal area was first explored by Captain Cook in 1770, and in 1788 England established the earliest Australian colony on the south shore of the Port Jackson Inlet.

As this scene makes evident, Port Jackson and the more northerly Middle Harbour are part of the drowned valley of the Parramatta River. The river can be traced west to its origin above the dark-blue starfish shape of Prospect Reservoir, which roughly marks Sydney's western limit. The city is built on the low plain of the Sydney Lowland Basin, seen here as blue, grey and light pink. The older urban development is found mainly south of the harbour, with the fine blue line of the famous Sydney Harbour suspension bridge, completed in 1932, marking the connection with the suburbs of North Sydney and Mosman. Taronga Park, home of Sydney's famous zoo, shows as a red patch in Mosman, east of the northern end of the bridge. Further north the dark brick-red of the 16,000-hectare (40,000-acre) Ku-ring-gai Chase National Park can be seen, extending all the way to the top of the picture.

East of Sydney is the south-facing Bondi Beach, its famous stretch of sand visible as a strip of white on the image. Due south lies Botany Bay, often maligned as the landing point for transported criminals (most landings in the nineteenth century were actually at Port Jackson). On the north shore of Botany Bay the projection of Sydney's international airport is clearly visible.

Below the bay we see the dark reds of another great park, this one the 14,000-hectare (34,000-acre) Royal National Park, and to the west of that is a military reserve. These areas are a marked contrast to the largely grassy plain south-west of Sydney. The Illawarra Mountains run along the coast below Botany Bay. As the direction of river flows makes clear, the watershed lies at the right-hand edge of the dark-red wooded area, close to the shore. Cataract, Cordeaux, and Avon Reservoirs are seen to be dammed at their western ends, where they flow to meet the north-running Nepean River. To the east, Warragamba Dam is also clearly visible at the northern end of Lake Burragorang.

Between the Illawarra Mountains and the sea a fertile grassy plain shows light pink on the image. It is narrow in the north and broadens as we move south to the large and shallow Lake Illawarra. The city of Wollongong, with Port Kembla just below it, shows blue-grey just above Lake Illawarra. Perhaps little known outside Australia, Wollongong is the continent's eighth largest city, with a population of 250,000. It serves as a shipping port for the dairy products of the fertile plain to the north, and also for the coal mined on the eastern slopes of the Illawarra Mountains. Port Kembla is a rapidly growing production town for iron and steel, and a developing centre for shipbuilding. Further south, below the lake, the light patch of the city of Shellharbour is a holiday resort town for Wollongong and Port Kembla.

Inland, on the left-hand side of the image, we see Lake Burragorang and the red wooded slopes of the Blue Mountains, an eastern spur of the Great Dividing Range. For many years during early colonization these steep ranges were the barrier to all development to the west.

Image scale and date: 1 cm = 4.1 km, October 1975.

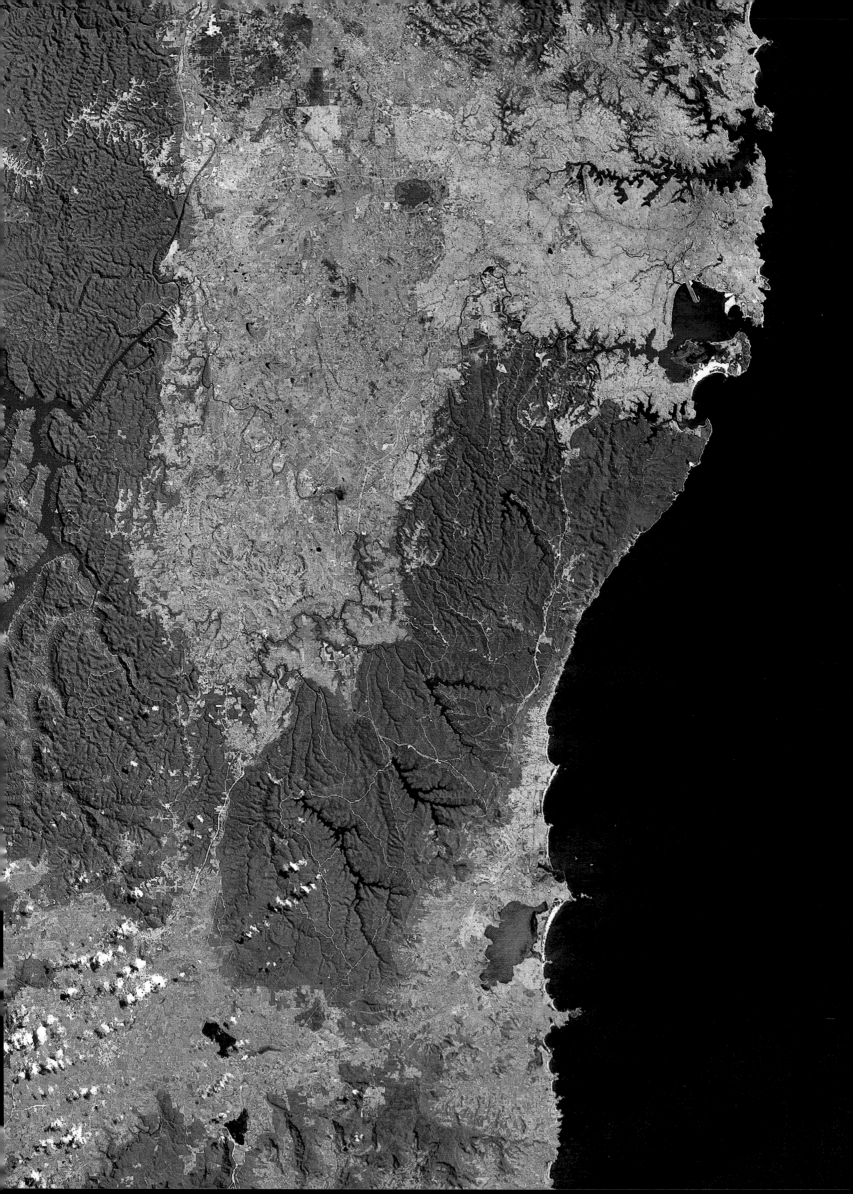

Vancouver

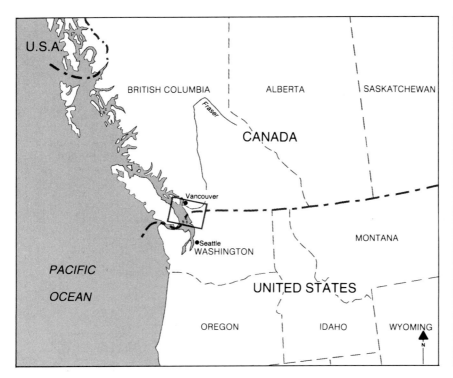

Canada's third largest city, principal Pacific seaport, and western terminus for the Canadian Pacific Railroad, Vancouver forms the industrial and commercial heart of the province of British Columbia. It is clearly visible near the centre of the left-hand side of the image, left of the meandering pale-blue snake of the Fraser River. The river is the largest in British Columbia. The great bright blue offshore smear in the black Strait of Georgia, below Vancouver, is produced by the large volume of sediment that the Fraser carries from the Cascade Mountains, whose westernmost snow-covered peaks are visible at the top of the image.

The city's population of just over 1 million has spread out from the area of the old city south to Lulu Island and north across Burrard Inlet. North Vancouver is seen here as a blue edging to the snow-covered Coast Mountains at the scene's left border. The Mount Seymour Provincial Park is visible on the left edge of the scene. Vancouver's numerous wharves and jetties can be seen on the right shore of Burrard Inlet, just above the projecting red peninsula of Stanley Park. Below and to the right of the city, piers and jetties, each about 5 kilometres long, are visible as blue lines jutting into the Strait of Georgia. At the end of the promontory below the city, the campus of the University of British Columbia shows as a bright red patch of Douglas fir and Western red cedar. To the right of this, on Sea Island, the runways of Vancouver's international airport show as a pattern of fine white lines. The brown oval patch to the right of Lulu Island is Burns Bog, a swampy undeveloped area from which peat is extracted.

The land above and to the right of Vancouver is part of the delta of the Fraser River. The soils here are up to 300 metres (1,000 feet) thick, and the regular geometric pattern of red fields is evidence of the area's fertility. Dairy, fruit, and vegetables are the main agricultural products. The U.S.-Canadian border passes right through the middle of the river delta, but unlike the Mexican border on the San Diego image, this political boundary is not visible on the image. The delta ends at Bellingham, seen as a blue patch on the coast. Further right, the blue-grey area around Mount Vernon is not urban development; it is cleared agricultural land.

Victoria, the administrative capital and until this century the largest city of British Columbia, lies below Mount Vernon, across the Georgia Strait. It is visible as a blue urban patch at the top of Vancouver Island. This picture covers only the eastern tip of the great island, which is 450 kilometres (280 miles) long and 130 kilometres (80 miles) wide, the biggest on the North American Pacific coast. It is largely covered with softwood forests, and the blue-grey areas in the island's centre are cleared timberlands.

Image scale and date: 1 cm = 5.3 km, July 1978.

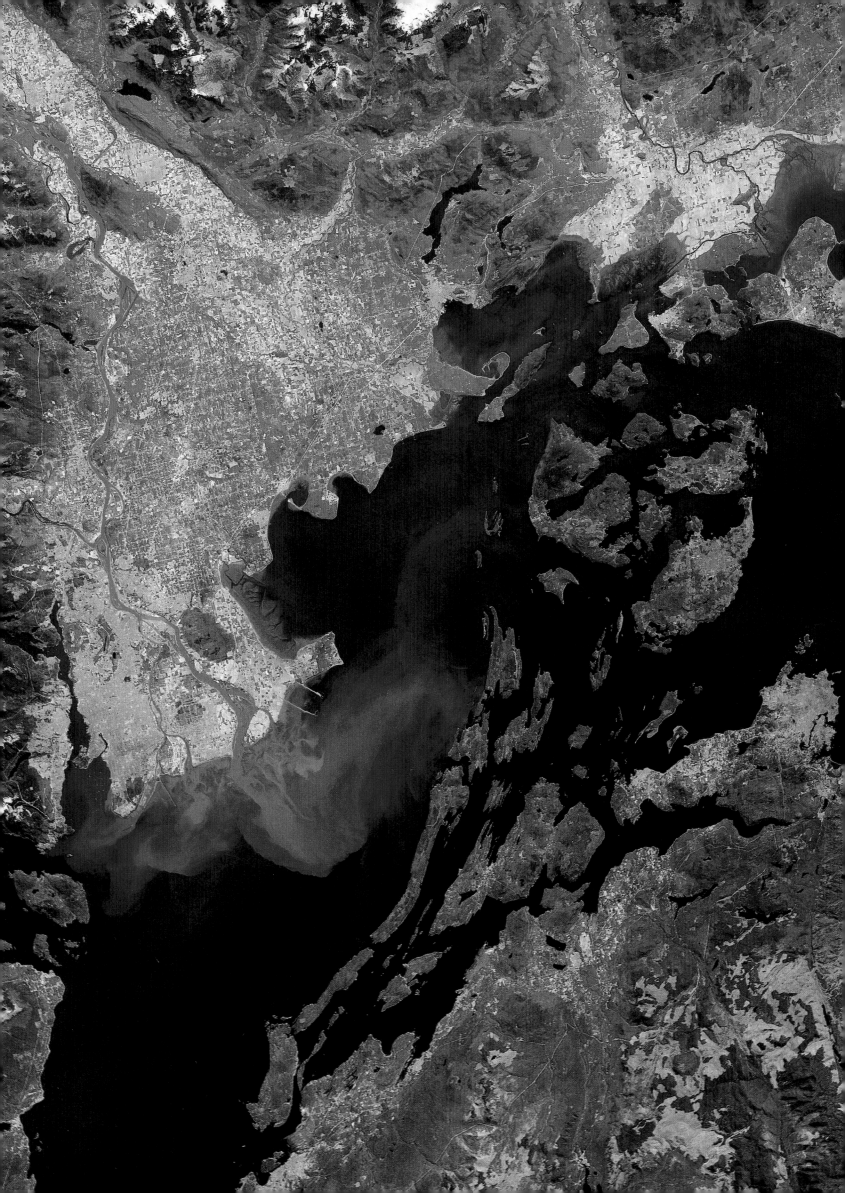

Energy and Minerals

Until maybe 5000 B.C., man was in balance with his environment. Every action made use of natural materials, and every product was returned to the land. It was the discovery that copper, and later bronze, could be used to produce tools and weapons that began the irreversible change.

Although the first ore deposits were pure metal, at or close to the surface, it was soon realized that far more copper, lead, and tin could be produced by smelting less concentrated ores, and that brass and bronze were often more useful than the individual elements from which they were produced. Thus subsurface mining and high-temperature processing evolved together. Today these twin factors — raw materials and the energy to manipulate them — are the driving force behind the extensive exploration programmes that are carried out by all industrial nations. Since abundant and inexpensive energy is also needed for the production of cheap agricultural fertilizers, the search for minerals and energy is of equal interest to the developing nations.

Over the centuries the nature of the exploration process has changed. The earliest deposits of precious metals, minerals, and fossil fuels lay close to centres of civilization, in shallow deposits and outcrops. As these were depleted, deeper mines were dug, and exploration gradually moved outward into less populated and less familiar territories. Much of the prospecting of the last four centuries was conducted by individual wanderers, lured on by the rumours of El Dorado, the Lost Legions, the Treasure of the Incas, and the Mother Lode. These men were the early explorers of the Sahara, of the Amazon basin, of the high Andes, and of the Yukon, living and often dying in the blank areas of the world map.

Today's explorers for fuels and minerals are of a different breed. All the easy targets for such resources have been probed, and now the search goes on in the most inaccessible regions of the world: in the sedimentary basins of the Arctic Islands north of Canada; along the North Slope of Alaska; beneath the shallow waters of the Java Sea, in the stormy seas off north-west Scotland, or at the bottom of the deep oceans; across the Tarim Basin, which includes the Takla Makan, one of the world's most extreme and feared deserts; in the South Atlantic on the continental shelf that extends past the Falkland Islands; and through the jungles of the Amazon.

Fortunately, today's geologist has new tools to help in the search, and Landsat images are among the most useful of these. They offer an unrivalled data base for general geological mapping, permitting a regional picture to be built up in advance of other exploration methods — even before a first field trip is made to a site of interest. It should be emphasized, however, that Landsat data are not a panacea, or a substitute for other exploration techniques such as seismic analysis, aeromagnetic surveys, and ground sampling. It is the combination of all these different methods that provides the 'convergence of evidence', the cross-checking of results that decreases exploration risks and costs.

Landsat data have another use when commercial deposits are discovered and processing begins. Many energy and mineral extraction processes greatly affect the environment, by massive ground disturbance (as in oilfield development and diamond mining), by the need for large quantities of water (as in tar sand oil extraction), and by thermal effects (in all extractive industries). Fortunately, the same image source that assisted in the discovery process proves equally valuable in monitoring the effects of subsequent development.

Bathurst Island, Canada

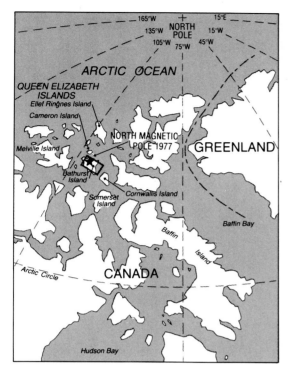

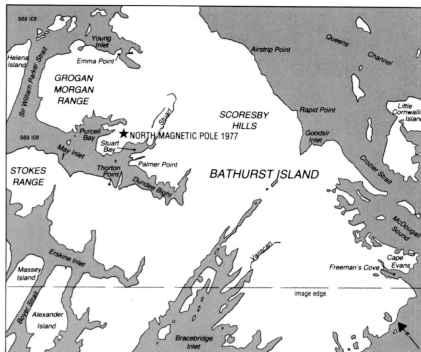

The bleak island shown in the image overleaf lies at almost 76 degrees north, far above Canada's Hudson Bay and the northern edge of the ancient Canadian Shield. Only the small island of Ellef Ringnes, north of the image area, stands between Bathurst Island and a clear run across the Arctic Ocean to the North Pole.

Bathurst Island is part of the Parry Islands group and lies 480 kilometres (300 miles) north-west of Baffin Island. Its long freezing winters and brief summers, its jagged shoreline surrounded even in midsummer by the broken pack ice visible on this image, and its bare, eroded, and glaciated surface make it appear an unlikely candidate for intensive energy resources exploration. But it is in fact an area of increasing geological interest. It sits near the centre of a huge sedimentary rock basin, 1,720,000 square kilometres (664,000 square miles) in area, incompletely explored but with all the geological elements to suggest that oil and gas should be found there in large quantities. The island sits at the intersection of two fold belts within the basin, the east-west trending Parry Islands Fold Belt, and the north-south trending Cornwallis Belt, and this picture shows clear evidence of both fold belt directions. The fold belts appear as curving zig-zags on the image. Folded rock formations, at depth, are prime candidates for oil and gas accumulation.

Most of Bathurst's surface, resembling in this image a great slab of polished marble, is a shale thinly covered with a layer of moss, lichen, and tough grasses. The remainder is composed of porous dolomitic limestones. Eroded and worn smooth by ancient glaciers, and too far north to be much weathered by the sun's day-night heating cycle, the surface of Bathurst stands as a textbook example of exposed anticlinal and synclinal structures, appearing on the image as the zig-zags referred to above.

Already there have been major finds of gas and oil-bearing sands in the Parry Islands. Melville Island, just to the west of the image, has high-pressure gas reservoirs in the Drake Point, Hecla and Winter Harbor fields; Ellef Ringnes, in the Sverdrup Basin to the north of the image, has gas (mostly methane) at Kristoffer Bay, Jackson Bay, and Wallis; and Cameron Island, just to the north-west, has the Bent Horn gas discovery. Promising drilling tests have been made on Bathurst itself by Sun Oil and by British Petroleum, at Dundee Bight on the lower end of May Inlet, and close to Freeman's Cove in the bottom right-hand corner of the image.

The blues and whites of massive ice are apparent on May Inlet, Sir William Parker Strait, and part of Erskine Inlet. Queens Channel is completely covered by masses of sea ice. Ice is the biggest impediment to rapid discovery and development, since many of the most interesting areas for drilling lie offshore, in the shallow ice-covered waters between the islands. However, on Bathurst Island another and less conventional difficulty is provided by polar bears. The animals are commonly found in the long fjord between Bracebridge Inlet and Goodsir Inlet, and apparently use this route as a convenient path in crossing the island.

One other feature lying within this image area, but not one perceptible to the Landsat system sensors, is the North Magnetic Pole. This location, towards which all magnetic compasses point, moves slowly but continuously on the surface of the earth. It currently lies in the northern part of Bathurst Island. A compass needle placed there will seek to move to a vertical position.

Image scale and date: 1 cm = 3 km, August 1977.

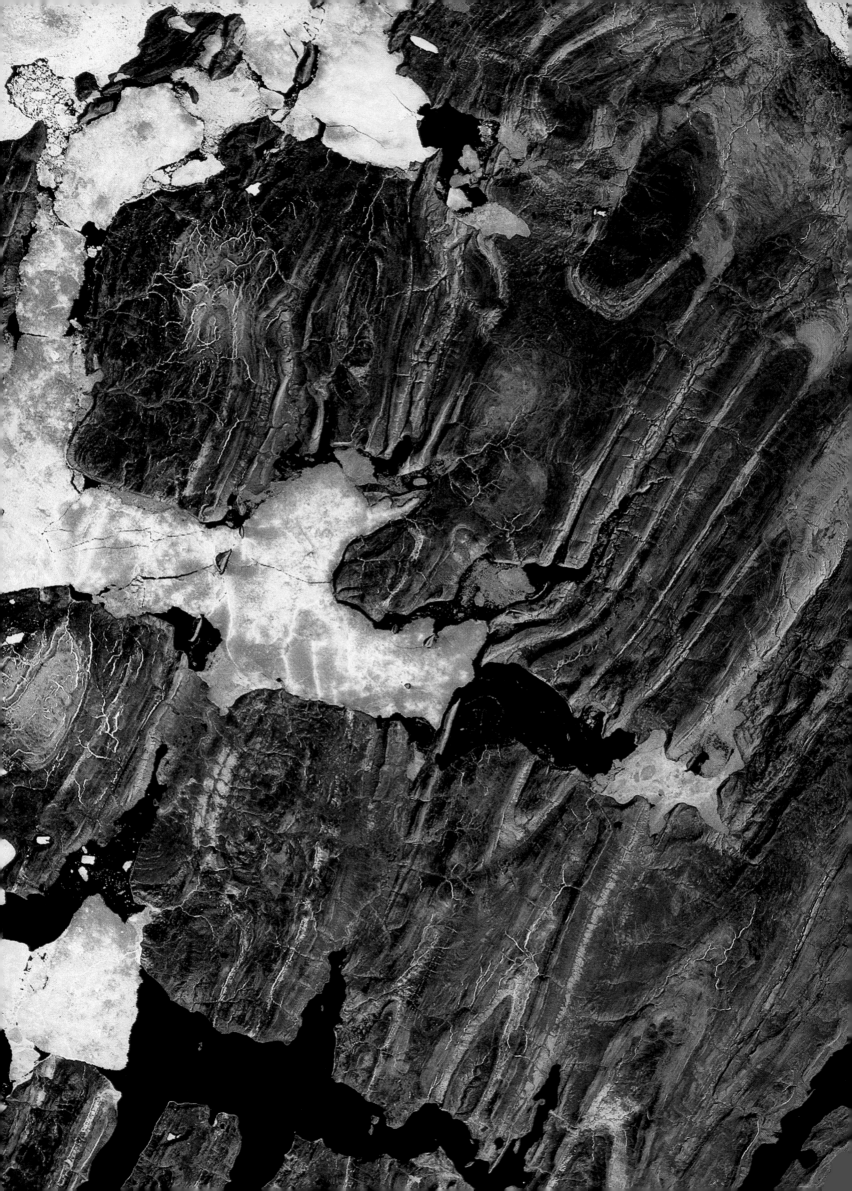

Bu Hasa Oilfield, United Arab Emirates

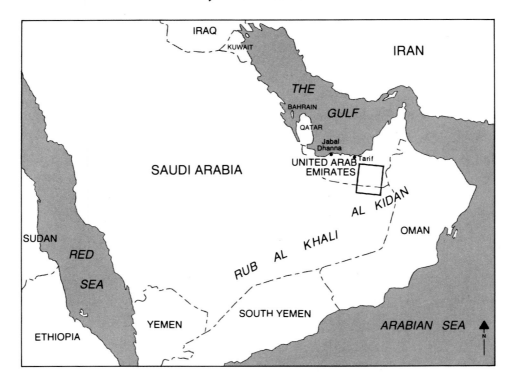

The Gulf is ringed by the world's richest oil-producing countries. The 'O.P.E.C. Circle' runs counterclockwise from Iran in the north-east, through Iraq, Kuwait, Saudi Arabia, Bahrain, and Qatar, and on to the United Arab Emirates and Oman on the southern Gulf shore. Together, these Middle East countries possess over half of the world's known oil reserves.

The Iran fields and those in Iraq were already well developed in the 1920s. However, it was the sensational oil strikes made in the 1930s by Standard Oil and Aramco in Bahrain and Saudi Arabia, and the similar pre-war successes of Gulf Oil and the Anglo-Iranian Oil Company in Kuwait, that made the southern and western Gulf shore the subject of continuous intensive exploration.

This image shows part of the United Arab Emirates. The Gulf lies just 24 kilometres (15 miles) north of the scene edge. The capital city of Abu Dhabi is 160 kilometres (100 miles) north-east, and the border of Oman is 160 kilometres due east. To the south lies the border with Saudi Arabia. The area is unbroken desert wilderness, notably lacking in signs of man's presence were it not for the great black smudge of an oil flare spreading across the upper part of the picture. Beneath the tan dunes lies the Bu Hasa oilfield, one of the U.A.E.'s biggest onshore petroleum resources. A 61-centimetre (24-inch) crude oil pipeline connects this field with the port town of Jabal Dhanna to the north-west, and the faint dark line of a road can be seen running off north-east towards Tarif, 72 kilometres (45 miles) away, also on the Gulf coast.

This scene lies on the northern flank of the desolate Rub al Khali, the 'Empty Quarter' that covers much of the Arabian Peninsula. Almost 650,000 square kilometres (250,000 square miles) in area, the Rub al Khali extends 1,300 kilometres (800 miles) from the U.A.E. right across southern Saudi Arabia to the border of Yemen. It is a great sea of sand, devoid of all vegetation and animal life. Several characteristic dune patterns can be seen in the lower half of the image. To the lower right lies the great sea-level *sabkha* of Al Kidan, a salt flat that shows in grey-blue patches among the brown cover of the dunes. The surface of the *sabkha* is composed of a thick, viscous clay, saturated with brine, that shows white as it dries completely. The sand-forms that sit above this salty crust are here of a type known as *barchan* dunes, folded crescent-shaped ridges that lie transverse to the prevailing winds. Soft and shifting, they are unusually difficult to cross with conventional transportation. To the left of the image the sands take on a completely different pattern. In this area they are *seif* dunes, long and thin, that run parallel to the direction of the prevailing winds.

Desolate as it may seem, this whole area is being intensively explored for oil. New finds have recently been reported within the salt-and-sand wilderness of Al Kidan itself.

Image scale and date: 1 cm = 4.9 km, November 1972.

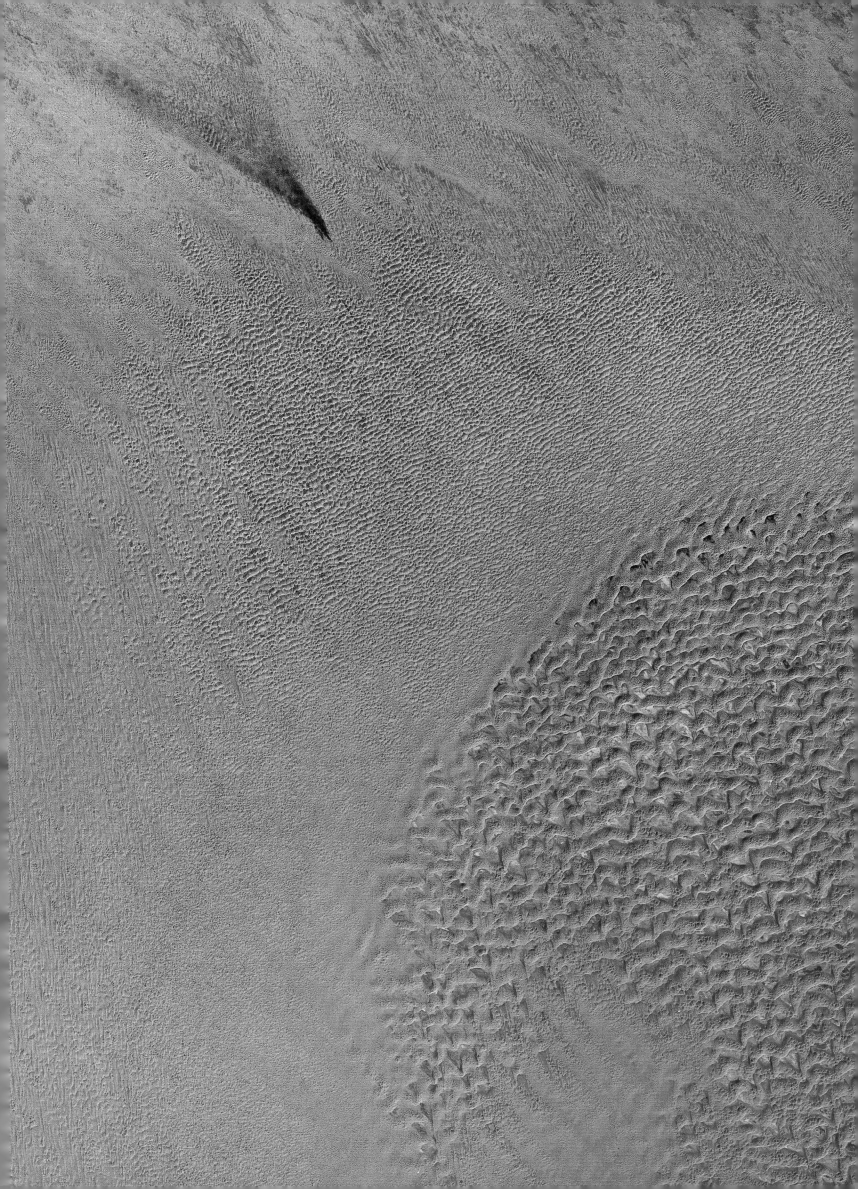

The Rustenburg Mines

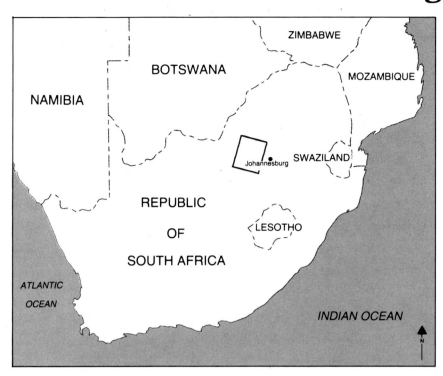

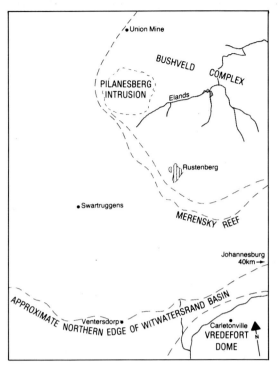

Platinum was not a substance known to and prized by the ancients. Its great value and widespread use in jewellery, electrical equipment and chemical processes date from the nineteenth century, 300 years after the Spanish discovery of large quantities of the metal in the sands of the South American Rio Pinto. Today, the world's largest known platinum deposits lie in the area covered by this image.

The picture covers part of the high veldt, the interior plateau that extends over most of South Africa's Cape Province. Johannesburg and Pretoria lie 40 kilometres (25 miles) to the east. The spectacular colours of the scene are rather typical of Landsat false-colour images of this part of South Africa, especially at the end of the summer (November to March) rainy season. The top left corner of the image covers an area that is dry and little vegetated, revealing the pale blue of alluvial deposits. The prominent circular feature at the top centre of the picture is the Pilanesberg syenite intrusion, a red mass of alkaline granite 24 kilometres (15 miles) in diameter that stands out from its surroundings because its fractured surface supports more vegetation.

The Bushveld Complex (see map) is an outcropping of iron and magnesium-rich rocks, capped by granites that are nearly 2,000 million years old, and it occupies most of the top right-hand corner of this scene. A variety of important mineral deposits occurs in and around the Complex. Chromium and vanadium, nickel, copper and tin are all mined in the area south and east of the town of Rustenburg. The most productive region for platinum, however, occurs along the famous Merensky Reef. It runs down from the top centre of the image, skirts the left-hand side of the Pilanesberg intrusion and curves across to the right-hand edge of the picture. The continuous outcropping of platinum-bearing rock was discovered by the geologist Hans Merensky in the 1920s. In the north of the image above the Pilanesberg intrusion the reef is not visible, but lower down, the system of rock units containing it is clearly visible as a light greenish-white tone, with a sharply defined red boundary below it. The Merensky Reef has been traced at surface outcrop for more than 240 kilometres (150 miles).

Platinum usually occurs together with a group of five other valuable materials, the 'platinum-group' metals: ruthenium, rhodium, palladium, iridium and osmium. Although all of these, together with some gold, are recovered from the Merensky Reef in commercial quantities, it is the four grams per tonne of platinum that justify the mining operations.

Near the bottom of the image the shadowy grey-green east-west lines of another geological formation are visible. These mark the approximate northern edge of the famous Witwatersrand Basin, an elliptical area 290 kilometres (180 miles) across that runs up to Johannesburg and contains South Africa's most productive deposits of gold and uranium. The realization of the economic value of the Witwatersrand deposits goes back to the 1880s, when the first gold-bearing outcrops were discovered on a farm near Johannesburg.

Below the northern limit of the Witwatersrand Basin, down in the lower right corner of the scene, another significant geological structure is visible. This is the north-west portion of the Vredefort Dome, an area of igneous rocks almost 80 kilometres (50 miles) across. Elements of its structure suggest that it could be the result of a long-ago meteor impact, but the fact that it also lies at the centre of the Witwatersrand Basin makes that conclusion open to suspicion.

Image scale and date: 1 cm = 5.8 km, March 1973.

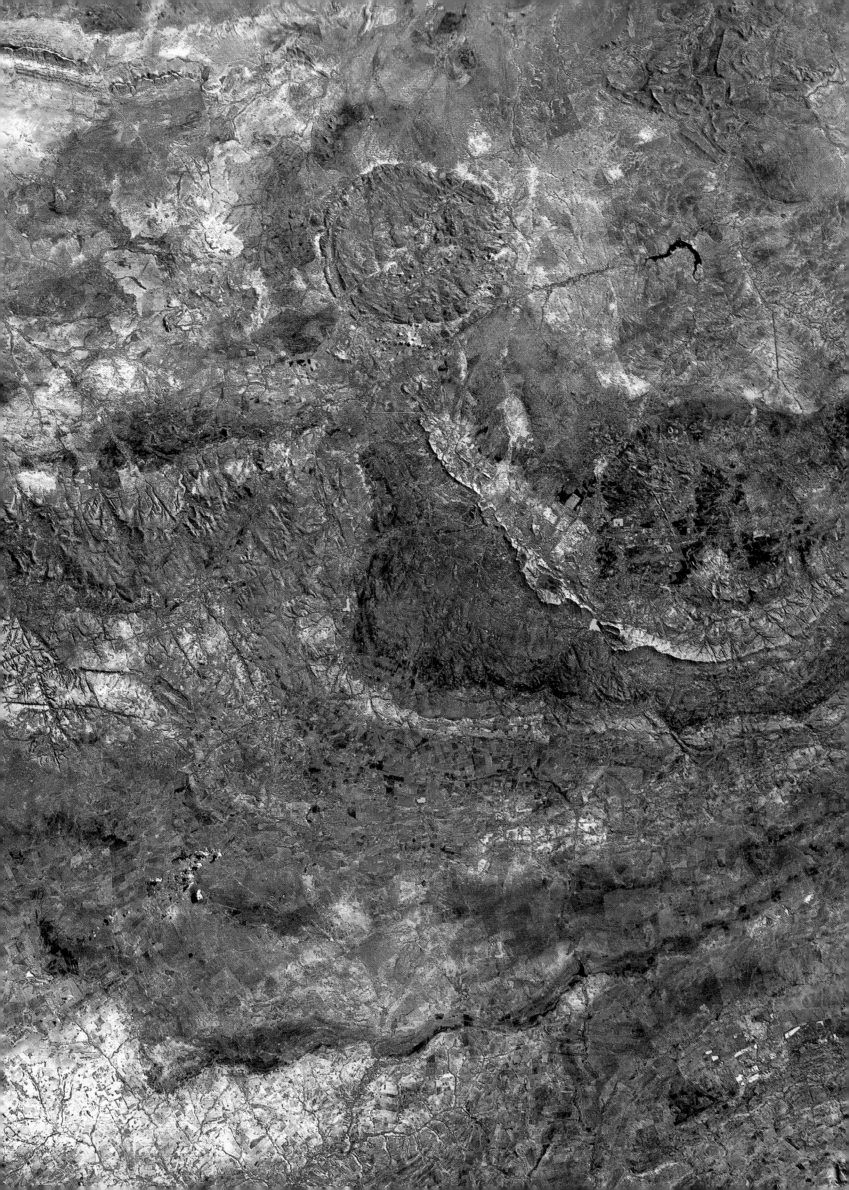

Cyprus

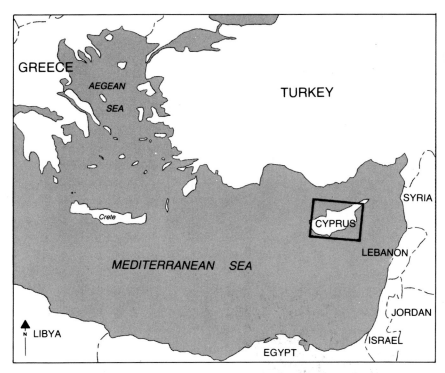

Copper was first used around 8000 B.C., well before the beginning of written history. About 5000 B.C. it was alloyed with tin to produce bronze, harder and tougher than copper alone, and the Bronze Age began. Soon after, brass was produced by alloying copper with zinc, and the bright metal came into common use for decoration. The demand for copper rose, and by 3000 B.C. the copper mines in Cyprus were already extensive and famous. The word 'copper' comes from the Latin word *cuprum* − *'aes Cuprium'*, the Cyprus ore. The Cyprus copper deposits were prized so highly that in ancient times the island was controlled successively by Egyptians, Assyrians, Phoenicians, Greeks, Persians, Romans and Syrians.

For modern Cyprus, seen here on this late spring image, copper is no longer the central support of the economy, although there are still operating mines. Most of them are located in 'pillow lava' formations at the northern and southern flanks of the central range of mountains, seen here as the large dark area in the middle of the island. Clouds overlie the highest peaks, which include the Troodos, with Mount Khionistra (Olympus) at 1,950 metres (6,400 feet) the highest point of the whole island. The general geological structure of Cyprus is displayed well on this scene, although the whole island, third largest in the Mediterranean, is a little too large to fit on a single Landsat scene. The central mountains, a great mass of dark, igneous rocks, extend from the bay at the bottom of the image almost to the coast at the top. The Kyrenia Mountains form a long, dark ridge along the whole left-hand side of the island, from Cape Kormakiti to the Karpas Peninsula beyond the top left-hand corner of the image. The Kyrenia Mountains, also known at their eastern end as the Karpas Mountains, are made of iron-rich Triassic redbeds, and limestones.

Between the Kyrenia and Troodos Mountains sits the main lowland of the island, the Mesaoria or Messaria Plain. The capital of Cyprus, Nicosia, can be seen as a darker patch in the centre of it. It is a city of 120,000; the island's total population is 640,000. The international airport is visible as a thin black line below and slightly to the right of Nicosia. To the right of the Troodos Mountains the foothills extend as a tan and grey area down to the coast. They are also made of lighter limestones and redbeds.

The principal ports of the island are at Famagusta, on the right-hand side of Famagusta Bay at the top of the image; Larnaca, on the lower shore of Larnaca Bay to the right; and Limassol, further down on Akrotiri Bay, left of the southern tip of Cyprus at Cape Gata. Two British naval bases are still maintained on the island, on the left side of Larnaca Bay and on Episkopi Bay, below Cape Gata.

Although the rainfall is light − about 40 centimetres (15 inches) a year − the whole island was once forested and timber was a leading export. It is clear from the brown and beige colours on the image that this is no longer the case. There are only three heavily vegetated areas, one at the bottom end of the Mesaoria Plain, one at the top below Cape Greco, and a small area right of Limassol. The grey patch to the right of the dark red vegetation is a shallow salt lake. The remaining woods on the island are oaks, cedars, olives, and cypresses, but they are mainly used domestically. The important commercial exports today are cotton, tobacco, wine, and a few minerals. The latter still includes some copper, but mineral exports are mainly asbestos, gypsum, and iron and copper pyrites.

Image scale and date: 1 cm = 5 km, May 1973.

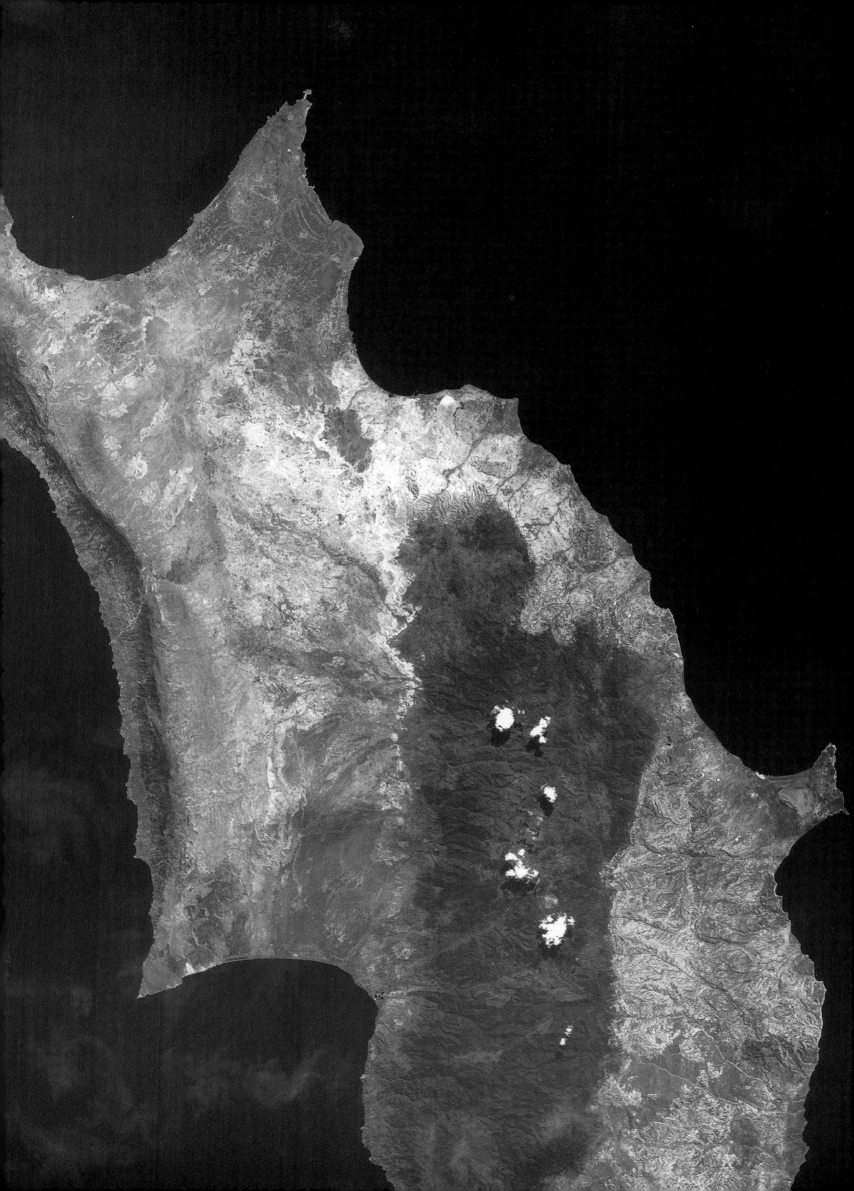

The Broken Hill Mines, New South Wales

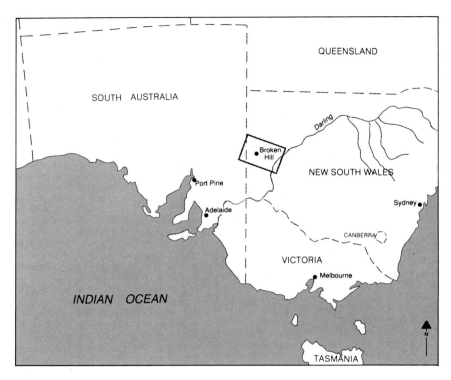

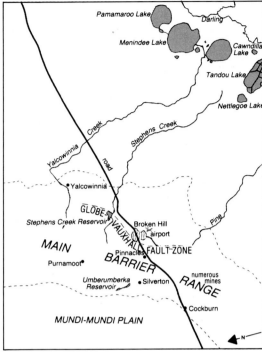

Broken Hill lies at the western edge of New South Wales, Australia, 420 kilometres (260 miles) north-east of Adelaide and 890 kilometres (550 miles) from Sydney. When the area was first explored by the Sturt expedition in 1844, dark rock outcrops of oxidized minerals were noticed at Broken Hill. However, serious prospecting did not begin until 1876, the main outcrop was not staked until 1883 (mistakenly, as a tin deposit!), and the first mine did not begin production until 1886. Today the area holds the world's leading known deposit of high-grade lead and zinc ores.

As the lack of red colour in the image makes clear, this is an arid, semi-desert part of the Australian interior. Rainfall is only 23 centimetres (9 inches) a year, and the vegetation, such as it is, consists of scrub, occasional trees, and short-lived drought-loving plants that flourish briefly after rain. There is some sheep-farming in the area, and the large rectangles over most of the scene are created by farm fencing.

Broken Hill is a bright patch of purple and blue colour near the middle of the image. It sits on a flat, elevated area of the Australian Pre-Cambrian Shield, about 300 metres (1,000 feet) above sea-level. The straight dark line running diagonally left to right across the image, through Broken Hill, is a road, flanked by rangeland. The dark curving line of the Globe-Vauxhall Fault Zone is also visible running through the lower left of the town. The blues and dark purples further down and to the left are slates and schists, part of the southern end of the Main Barrier Range. Beyond the clearly-defined dark edge of the range lie the browns and tans of the Mundi-Mundi Plain, a desert region of sands and sedimentary rocks. The small bright-red patch to the left of Broken Hill is vegetation on the surface of Stephens Creek Reservoir.

At the upper right of the scene lies an eye-catching series of water bodies known as the Menindee Lakes. Lakes Pamamaroo, Menindee, Cawndilla, Tandou and others beyond the image area are part of the Darling River watershed which runs east from here to drain the north-west edge of the Murray Basin. The lakes are shallow, and Lake Tandou shows a brightly-coloured pattern of salt pans. As this image shows, the creeks that flow towards the lakes from the left of Broken Hill in normal years never reach them; instead, they terminate in the parched lands below the lakes. However, the faint line of Yalcowinnia Creek can be traced all the way to Lake Cawndilla, from the line of vegetation that follows the stream bed.

The mines at Broken Hill, and at Pinnacles 16 kilometres (10 miles) to the south-west, contain a very rich ore. Although the main outcrop of lead-zinc sulphide lies within a tightly folded lens-shaped volume less than 6.5 kilometres (4 miles) long and only 150 metres (500 feet) across, the million tons of ore it produces each year is more than 13 per cent lead, better than 11 per cent zinc, and has substantial recoverable amounts of other materials: 60,000 tonnes a year of sulphur; 200 tonnes of cadmium; 140 tonnes of silver; and lesser amounts of gold, cobalt, copper and antimony. The ore is milled here at Broken Hill, to yield a lead concentrate and a zinc concentrate. Then it is shipped 320 kilometres (200 miles) to Port Pirie in South Australia, where most of the lead concentrate is smelted and refined. The zinc concentrate is shipped overseas, mainly to Hobart, Tasmania, and to Swansea, Wales, for extraction of zinc and cadmium.

Just to the right of the multi-coloured oval of Broken Hill the airport can be seen as a small white triangle.

Image scale and date: 1 cm = 5.2 km, November 1980.

The Athabasca Tar Sands, Alberta

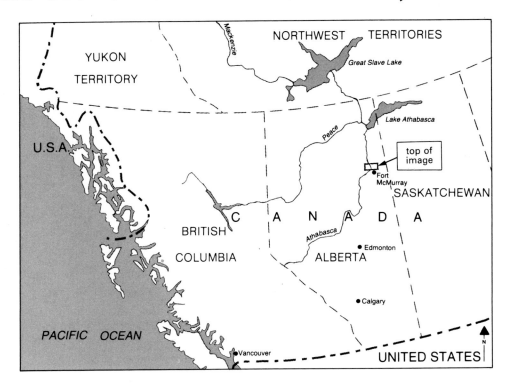

As supplies of high-quality light oil dwindle, the world's deposits of heavy oils, tars, and bitumens attract increased commercial interest. The world's greatest known pool of high-quality tar sands lies beneath the ground area covered by this image. The scene is north-west Alberta, with Edmonton 370 kilometres (230 miles) to the south-south-west and Lake Athabasca about 210 kilometres (130 miles) to the north. The blue line of the Athabasca River cuts through the centre of the picture, and vast tar sand extraction facilities can be seen below it.

This scene covers the centre of the Athabasca Deposit, a 34,000-square-kilometre (13,000-square-mile) subterranean pool of tar-filled sands stretching almost 320 kilometres (200 miles) from north to south and 160 kilometres (100 miles) from east to west. The McMurray Formation that contains the tars is as deep as 460 metres (1,500 feet) in many places, but near the centre of this scene it is found less than 15 metres (50 feet) below the surface. That is fortunate, because the thick, tarry oil held within the pores of the sand like water in a sponge cannot be pumped. It is a dense, viscous bitumen, and it will not flow except at high temperatures. Instead, the tar sands must be mined, like a mineral, and the oil extracted from them in surface processing plants.

Although the original discovery of the field was made in 1788 from surface outcrops, less than 10 per cent of the total tar sands of the Athabasca Deposit lie close enough to the surface to be mined. This still provides proven reserves of about 75,000 million barrels. For comparison, the Prudhoe Bay field of Alaska, one of the world's ten largest oil pools, contains about 15,000 million barrels. The Athabasca Deposit is unusually rich, with extractable oils making up about 35 per cent by volume of the tar sands.

The natural ground cover of the image area is poor-quality forest, consisting of black spruce and tamarack brush on a muskeg surface. The cleared white areas below the river are places where surface cover has been removed, the soil overburden cleared off, and the 45-metre-thick (150-foot) tar sands transported to the processing plants. There the sands are agitated in hot water, the oil rises to the top, and the sands sink to the bottom. After processing, the oil (termed 'synthetic crude') is transported by pipeline to Edmonton. The pipeline route and its associated service roads are visible as white lines below the river on the right of the extraction plants. The residual sands, after passing through the light-blue tailing ponds, are mixed with organic matter and fertilizer and returned to the surface in an environmental recovery programme.

Two different companies operate plants in the area shown: Syncrude Ltd, and Great Canadian Oil Sands. Together, these two groups produce over 150,000 barrels a day of synthetic crude oil, and move more than 750,000 tonnes of solid surface to do so. In order to operate economically, the tar sand extraction facilities must run continuously, twenty-four hours a day and 365 days a year. In the next twenty-five years, estimated total production will be well over 1,000 million barrels. If improved extraction methods permit the use of the deeper parts of the Athabasca Deposit, reserves from this single field would be close to 900,000 million barrels.

Image scale and date: 1 cm = 2 km, August 1981.

The Chott Jerid of Southern Tunisia

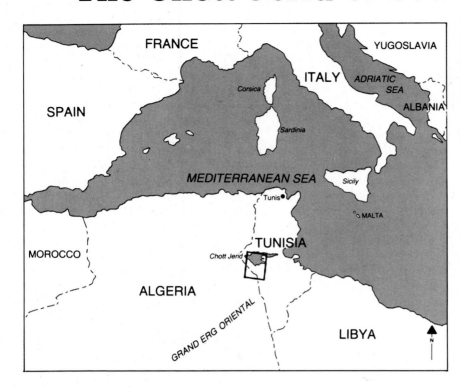

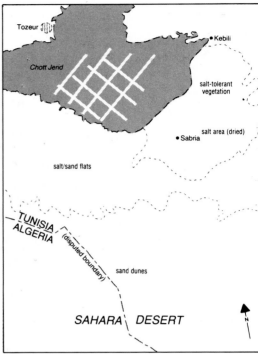

Although the country of Tunisia is quite narrow, so that no location within it is more than 350 kilometres (220 miles) from the sea, this image has the appearance of a true interior desert. It lies on the Tunisian western border with Algeria, about 400 kilometres (250 miles) south-west of the capital city of Tunis. Although the coastal parts of the country are fertile plains, with adequate rainfall for farming, this scene lies at the edge of the Tunisian Sahara, to the north of the great sandy area known as the Grand Erg Oriental. The striking pattern of dunes seen on the lower right of the image extends south for hundreds of kilometres.

The large eye-catching purple area at the top is the Chott Jerid, a vast salt pan that lies 15 metres (50 feet) below sea-level. It is surrounded by a row of oases, famous for their dates, and one such settlement, at Tozeur, is visible as a dark red patch at the upper left of the scene. With perhaps only 10-15 centimetres (4-6 inches) of rain a year, and that uncertain in time of arrival, there is no other vegetation anywhere in the scene except for occasional scrub grass, saltbush, and acacias. There is no vegetation at all within the Chott Jerid itself, and the 'field boundaries' clearly visible within the Chott must be given some other explanation. They are in fact part of the persistent and on-going search for oil and gas deposits in southern Tunisia; specifically, they are dynamite seismic lines.

One of the key requirements for successful oil and gas exploration is a knowledge of the subsurface structure of rock layers; in particular, how do different layers rise and fall in depth at different locations? One way to answer this question would be through a drilling programme, analysing the rock core obtained from each hole to build up a subsurface picture. This is prohibitively expensive. Seismic exploration is more economic. Shock waves are initiated at the surface of the ground, using explosive charges or direct impact with a very heavy object. These shock waves will be partially reflected, refracted, and diffracted by changes in material, and by rock-layer discontinuities. The signal that is returned to the surface can be measured by instruments known as geophones. If a whole series of such charges is exploded one after another along a line on the ground, the set of returned signals can be applied (after a great deal of work with computers) to make inferences about the structure directly beneath. In practice, a regular grid of such lines is used to build up the whole subsurface pattern and to decrease the uncertainty of the results.

The pattern visible in the Chott Jerid is the result of a series of dynamite charges, setting up a seismic exploration grid with an 8-kilometre (5-mile) spacing on the ground. The flat, even crust of the salt pan leads to a completely regular, ruled appearance on the Landsat image. It is unlikely that the visible pattern is due to the explosions themselves, although a dynamite charge in a swampy area will often cause a spreading geyser of mud. More likely we are seeing the tracks of 'swamp buggies', the broad-wheeled vehicles that cross the brittle salt crust to place charges and geophones. Ordinary vehicles cannot be used, because beneath that crust lies a muddy, hypersaline brine, into which narrow wheels will sink. In ancient times the Chotts of southern Tunisia were bodies of water. Although today they have salt crusts hard enough in places to support a caravan, the native Arabs tell of camels lost in the briny under-ooze when they strayed off the known safe paths.

Image scale and date: 1 cm = 5.3 km, February 1976.

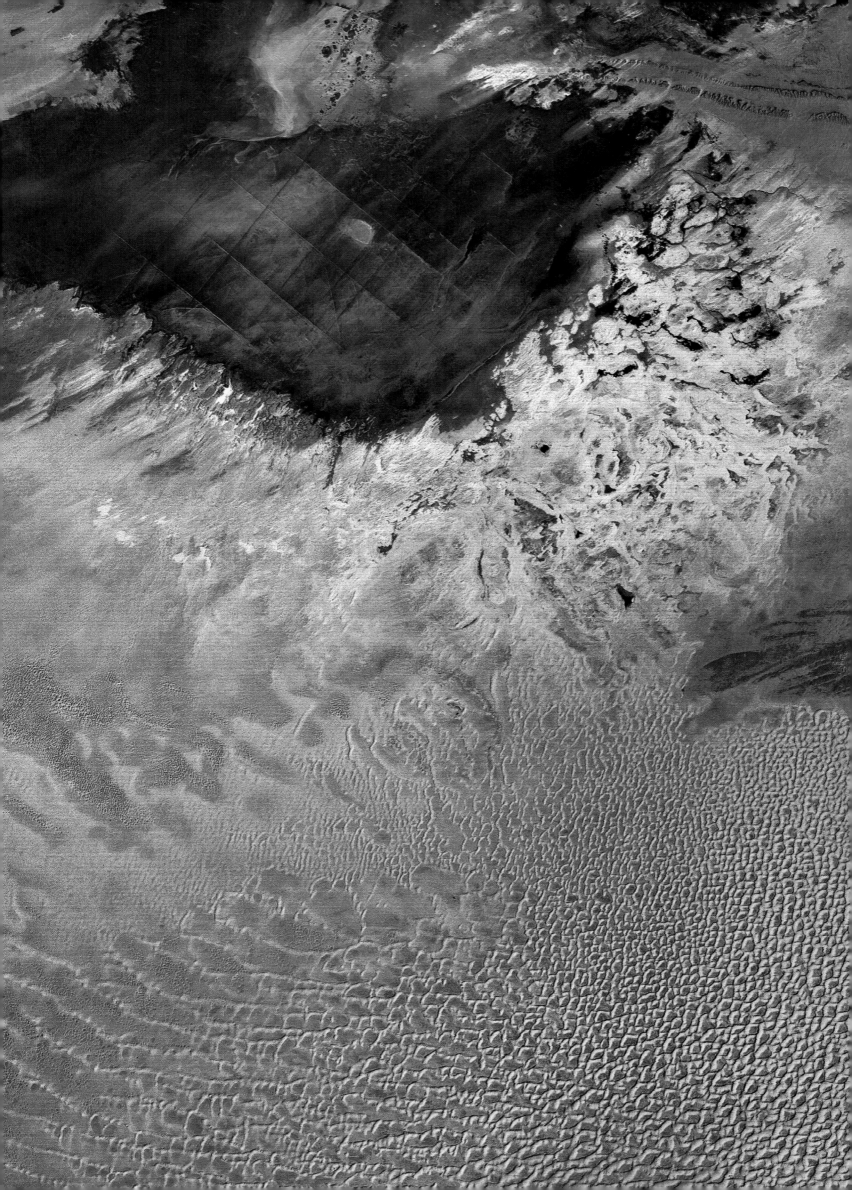

The Orange River Diamond Mines

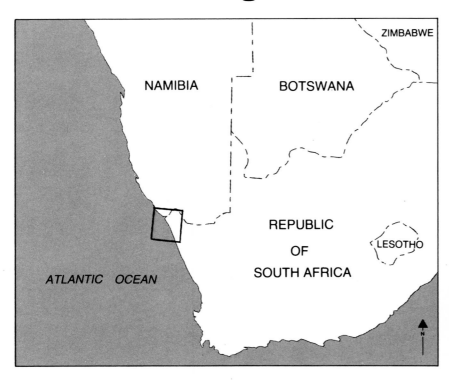
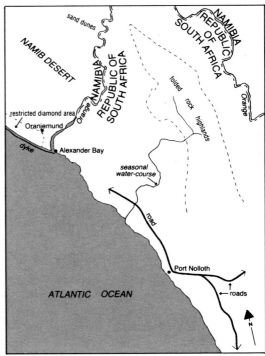

The cold Benguela Current, sweeping north past the coast of west Africa, dictates the climate of the area of this image. Onshore winds are too chilly to carry much rain, although they provide generous amounts of fog and drizzle. Offshore winds are dry after the long run across the continent. The result is a desert, one that runs along much of the west side of southern Africa, and rainfall along the coast of only about 5 centimetres a year.

This scene shows the Orange River at the border between South Africa and Namibia. Where the black and red thread of the river meets the Atlantic Ocean the world's greatest deposits of alluvial diamonds are located. This is literally a case where diamonds are strewn on the ground like pebbles. The gems are found in the gravel of fossil marine beds, along a broad stretch of the coastline that runs from Oranjemund, above the Orange River, north-westward for hundreds of kilometres. Other big alluvial diamond deposits are found at Alexander Bay, south of the river, and at Kleinzee, just below the bottom of the image area. Port Nolloth (not visible) is at the top end of the lower large white sand area on the image, which is of different origin and constituency from the ancient yellow sand deposits in the interior. The white line of the road from Port Nolloth to Alexander Bay is evident for most of the way, until it is lost in white sand tones.

The first diamond discovery was made at Oranjemund in 1908. In 1927 the known productive area was greatly increased. Since then, production has grown to more than 1.5 million carats of diamonds a year − over a quarter of a tonne of gem-quality stones. To find 30 grams (1 oz) of diamonds, more than 2,000 tonnes of sand and gravel must be excavated and sifted. The operations to accomplish this are elaborate and on a massive scale, and the signs of that work show on the image as a series of fine lines perpendicular to the shore, north and south of the Orange River mouth. These are open pits worked with huge bulldozers, draglines, and earth-moving machinery, protected from the ocean by a great seashore dyke which is visible as a fine grey line running up from the mouth of the Orange River. Mining is also being extended offshore, using barges to dredge and filter sediments.

Despite the competition from new forms of simulated diamonds, notably the cubic zircons produced in Taiwan and Korea, high-grade large-carat diamonds remain one of the principal exports from South Africa, which at present operates all the diamond mines covered by this image.

Inland from the mines there is little to see but desert. Although the Orange River, with a length of 1,859 kilometres (1,155 miles) and a watershed of 440,000 square kilometres (170,000 square miles), is South Africa's largest watercourse, it is too variable in flow to support agriculture in its western parts. Plans to dam it near Oranjemund may change this, but for the moment this whole area remains as the southern edge of the Namib Desert, whose 300-metre-high (1,000-foot) sand dunes roll away to the border of Angola, 1,300 kilometres (800 miles) to the north. The desert vegetation, such as it is, consists of desert grasses and low thorn bushes that grow along the dry riverbeds. The heavier patches of red vegetation that show along the banks of the Orange River are mostly woodybush, or karroobush, which seeds rapidly after rain and can if necessary survive a nine-month drought. In the eastern portion of the image, differential erosion in folded ancient rock highlands has created the rugged aspect of the landscape.

Image scale and date: 1 cm = 5.3 km, February 1981.

82

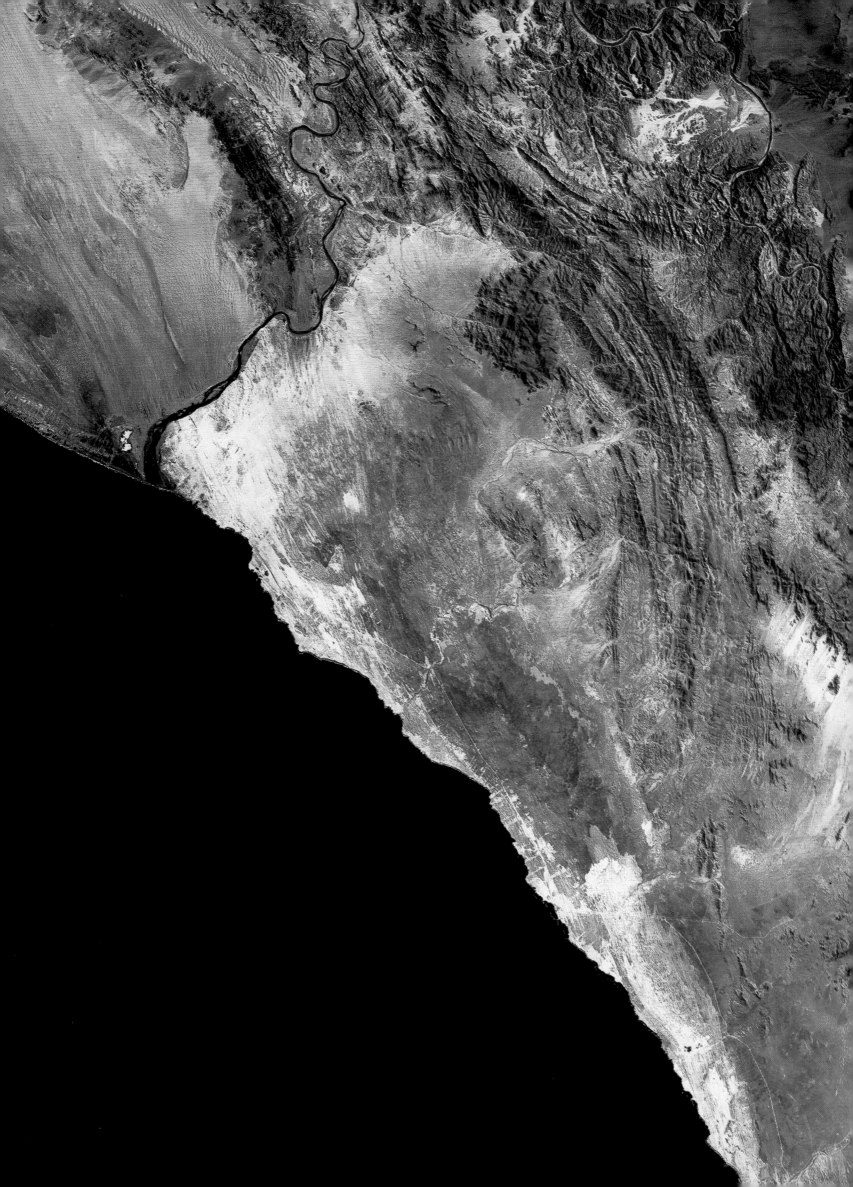

Texas Oilfields

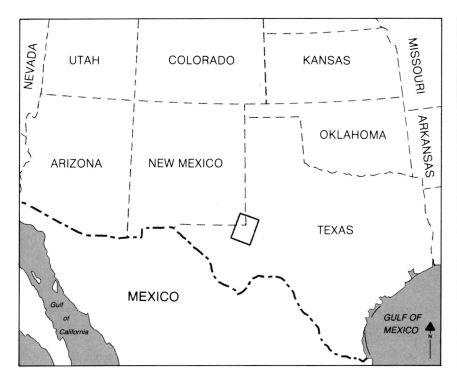

The first recorded oil production in Texas was in 1889, but it was far from here. This corner of the state, where it meets New Mexico, was considered unpromising oil country. Until 1920 the dry, undulating plateau shown in the image remained almost unexplored. The Pecos River, at the bottom of the picture, was too intermittent and unreliable in its flow to encourage agriculture, and the whole area remained low in population.

In 1920, an almost random drilling in Mitchell County, over 160 kilometres (100 miles) east of the image area, discovered the Westbrook Pool, and oil production began. Encouraged by that result, Texon Oil and Land Company initiated an almost equally unscientific drilling programme, leading to the discovery in 1923 of the Big Lake field in Reagan County, about 80 kilometres (50 miles) east of the image area. By the end of 1925 that field was producing 32,000 barrels a day, and full-scale geological exploration of west Texas was under way. The Wheat oilfield in Loving County, the Jal, Rhodes and West Eunice fields in Lea County (New Mexico), and the Hendricks (now Hendrick-Kermit-Scarborough) field in Winkler County, all lie within this image area. They were discovered in the mid-1920s, and by 1930 there was a general realization that this whole region is underlain by vast petroleum reserves, comprising the West Texas and South-east New Mexico Permian Basin. In the fifty years since first production, 12,000 million barrels of oil and thousands of millions of cubic metres of natural gas have been pumped from these fields.

Evidence of extensive oil and gas fields is provided on the image, particularly in the north-east, by the grid-like pattern of thousands of white dots, each one associated with a ground disturbance produced by drilling. As the number of wells suggests, we are looking at a part of one of the world's greatest petroleum provinces. The upper right of the scene lies in the Central Basin Platform, and the lower left in the Delaware Basin. Both are prolific producers.

Additional discoveries, often at greater depths, continued through the 1930s and 1940s. Within the image area are Fuhrman and Deep Rock fields in the north-east; Hendrick-Kermit-Scarborough in the centre; Goldsmith and Harper to the right; and O'Brien, Estes, and Shipley in the bottom right-hand corner of the picture. A new field at Monahans, in the south-east quadrant, was found at 3,000-metre (10,000-foot) depth in 1942, and the Kermit and Keystone fields, in the centre of the scene, were deepened in 1943. Most of the wells throughout the whole Permian Basin have proved to have unusually good producing lifetimes, often as long as forty years.

Apart from the oilfields, there is little to catch the eye in this scene. The white, chalky-looking areas near the scene centre are sand hills; the Monahans Sand Hills State Park is at the lower end of them, and the towns of Pecos, Kermit, Jal, and Andrews all show as small darker patches against the tan, unvegetated surface. The scene is scattered with small, disused airfields that grew up here during and after the Second World War because the clear skies and uniform weather permitted military pilots many hours of flying practice. The south-west and south-east corners along the Pecos River, and the darker patch in the centre, show some agriculture, encouraged now by the river control of Red Bluff Reservoir, off the image to the west.

Image scale and date: 1 cm = 4.2 km, December 1972.

Uranium in the San Rafael Swell, Utah

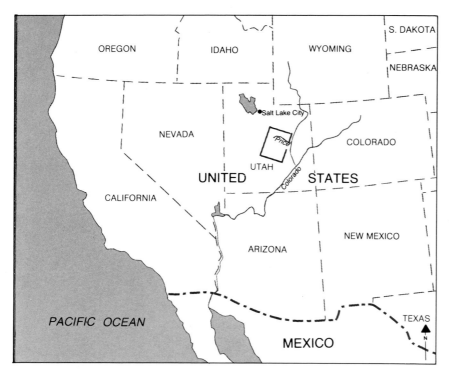
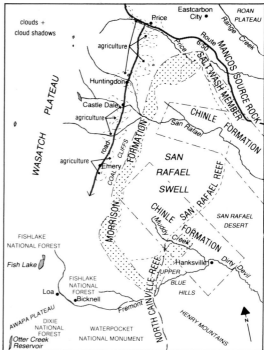

The image area shown here lies in central Utah, 130 kilometres (80 miles) south-east of Salt Lake City. The oval feature that dominates the central part of the picture is the San Rafael Swell. This is a plateau formed from an eroded dome, whose bleak canyons became the prehistoric home of the cave-dwelling Anasazi Indians after attacks from other tribes forced them to move here from the Roan Plateau, visible at the upper right corner of the scene. The original Anasazi have long since vanished, to be replaced in Utah by the modern Pueblo Indians. Today the San Rafael Swell is an area of great interest for uranium exploration.

Interpretation of the colours of this image must be done with unusual care since it has been specially computer-processed to accentuate the differences between different surface-rock types. The result is extremely useful, if rather unfamiliar and spectacular in appearance. The Swell is the golden-brown central area of sedimentary rocks, cut through by black and white lacy patterns of gullies and dry riverbeds. At the top right of the central oval lies a broad band of shale, displayed here as blue. Routes 50 and 6 (the same road at this point) can be seen running along the length of this blue swath, and there is a minor road running along the blue and pink on the other side of the Swell. The Denver and Rio Grande Western Railway runs parallel to, but is indistinguishable from, Routes 50 and 6. Thin layers of golden-brown within the blue shale to the left of the Swell indicate layers of sandstone. Further left, areas of light pink within the band of blue are vegetated alluvial fans, watered by the brighter fuchsia-coloured mountains to the west. These fans are the only areas of the scene that can be farmed. The fans run along Coal Cliffs, from the town of Emery in the middle of the scene to Price at the upper edge.

To the right of the Swell lies the yellow-brown San Rafael Desert, cut by the dark dendritic pattern of the Dirty Devil River near the lower right of the scene. Its tributaries, Fremont River to the south and Muddy Creek to the north, are further left on the image. The separation of the Swell from the desert is marked by the blue-white ragged line of the San Rafael Reef, which forms the eastern border of the Swell. It runs south to the left of the Upper Blue Hills which are displayed (suitably) as bright blue. At this point the reef becomes known as the North Caineville Reef and runs on down past the Henry Mountains, here seen as a light rose colour.

To the west the scene shows part of the Wasatch Plateau, also rose coloured, with the deeper fuchsia tints of the Fishlake National Forest visible below and to the right of the plateau, and the Dixie National Forest lower down on the bottom edge of the image. The dark area of the Awapa Plateau can be seen in the lower left-hand corner of the picture.

Two different formations around the San Rafael Swell contain known uranium-bearing rocks, and are currently being actively explored. The Chinle Formation, Triassic layers of sandstone, claystone and siltstone, occurs in two broad strips (seen as striped areas on the map), one centred on the San Rafael River, and the other beginning at the Dirty Devil River and extending north-west into the Swell. No uranium is yet being mined there. The claystones and sandstones of the Jurassic Morrison Formation occur at several different places within this scene (see map). Uranium oxide is now being mined from the Salt Wash Member of the formation, in the Green River District of the Swell. Several thousand tonnes have been produced in the past ten years.

Image scale and date: 1 cm = 5.8 km, September 1974.

Strategic Pressure Points

The written history of mankind is largely a story of intrigue, battles, and the struggle between tribes and nations for territories and economic advantage. The role that remote observation of an enemy could play in war was recognized very early, so that Galileo, writing to the Doge of Venice in the early 1600s regarding the recent discovery of the telescope, could remark: 'At sea, we shall be able to see enemy warships and their flags two hours before they see us . . . on land it should be possible from high places to observe enemy camps and their fortifications . . .'

Space provides a 'high place' that Galileo perhaps never dreamed of, a unique vantage point from which one nation can observe another's activities. Reconnaissance satellites, or 'spy satellites', are a widely known if little mentioned reality of today's world. An idea of their capabilities can be gained by noting that the Space Telescope, scheduled for 1985 launch, will carry a 2.4 metre telescopic mirror. The instrument will be used exclusively for looking *outward*, at astronomical targets; however, it could just as well be used to look down at the earth's surface. Used in that mode it would in principle allow objects as small as 5 centimetres across to be seen on the ground. The earth's atmosphere would somewhat degrade that performance, because in addition to absorbing and scattering part of the light, it is in small-scale continuous motion that blurs an image. Even so, the Space Telescope could certainly resolve objects less than half a metre across; and the Space Telescope is not at the limit of modern instrument technology for spaceborne observing systems.

Seen from this perspective, the Landsat spacecraft, with their sensors that see only objects many tens of metres and more across, provide a very poor instrument for space-spying. This is by design. When the Earth Resources Survey Program was established by N.A.S.A. in 1965, there was a sensitivity to the concern of many nations that they might suffer continuous surveillance from space. The inability of the first Earth Resources spacecraft to study features smaller than a football field was a compromise choice, a capability that would allow useful resource analysis to be performed without arousing international opposition. In addition, the programme was operated under an 'open skies' policy, so that images could be ordered by anyone, of any part of the world.

The N.A.S.A. policy has paid off and international objections to the programme have dwindled as the value of Landsat data has been increasingly recognized. Today, Landsat spacecraft are flying with instruments that provide twice the detail of the first models. In 1984, the French S.P.O.T. (Système Probatoire d'Observation de la Terre) satellite will provide even better detail and reveal objects as small as 10 metres across. This trend will continue. By the year 2000 it is hard to imagine that there will be any limits on resolution of spaceborne sensors, other than those imposed by the technical state-of-the-art of the future optical systems.

Meanwhile, we must settle for a view that reveals other aspects of war and strategy. The present Landsat spacecraft allow us to observe centres of military power and global pressure points; to traverse key communications corridors; to look at sites of weapons development and deployment; and to visit old (and some not-so-old) battlegrounds. This is perhaps more than enough evidence of war from a system that was conceived, built, and operated as a purely civilian service.

Aden and the Strait of Mandab

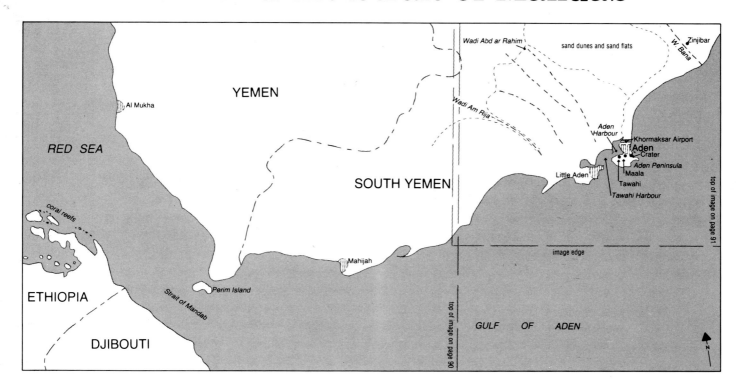

Aden, with its fine natural harbour and location close to the entrance to the Red Sea, forms a logical point for refuelling of ships on their way from Europe to the Orient. It is also a strategic base for control of southern access to the Suez Canal and Mediterranean Sea.

The two images shown on the following pages overlap, although they are presented at different scales and were recorded in different years. Four countries are visible on the first scene: Ethiopia and Djibouti, whose boundary lies in the cloud-covered area to the right of the Strait of Mandab, just above the blue coral reefs; Yemen (Yemen Arab Republic) on the other side of the strait, lower left; and South Yemen (People's Democratic Republic of Yemen, formerly Aden) in the upper left of the image. The border between Yemen and South Yemen runs up to the left from the narrowest point of the Strait of Mandab, with Perim Island, off the tip of the headland, part of South Yemen. The second scene lies entirely in South Yemen.

The images display a flat blue-grey coastal plain, traversed by the light lines of numerous dry wadis. A few swaths of red vegetation occur along seasonal streams that flow out of the mountains, to permit one crop per year using flood irrigation methods. Inland from the plain lies a more rugged area, rising to 2,000 metres (6,500 feet) and showing the pink of light vegetation. There is little sign of systematic agriculture, although the Yemen hills visible above the Red Sea are the most fertile part of the whole arid Arabian Peninsula. Cereals are grown here, as well as figs, fruit, walnuts, cotton (the main export), and *qat,* an alkaline narcotic that comes from the shrub *Catha edulis* and is used widely in Yemen and South Yemen. Coffee is also grown in the hills, and *mocha* coffee takes its name from Mocha (Al Mukha), on the coast.

Other than agriculture and fishing, the area has few productive industries. The region is composed of ancient fractured granites, partly covered by sedimentary limestones and sandstones, and it has no known oil or mineral deposits. Both Yemens have a negative balance of payments, and the standard of living is very low.

The situation was different prior to 1967, before British withdrawal from Aden and the independence of South Yemen. Since 1839, when Aden first became a British colony, most of the country's industry and supplies had derived from foreign ships using Aden as a free port and as a bunkering site on the way east. With the opening of the Suez Canal in 1869, Aden became one of the world's leading coaling ports. Later, when merchant fleets changed to oil for fuel, British Petroleum built in 1954 a large refinery on Little Aden, capable of processing 5 million tonnes of crude oil a year. The country's economic situation worsened in the 1960s and 1970s with the interruption of traffic through the Suez Canal and with British use of alternative facilities to serve naval needs in the Indian Ocean.

The image shows good detail within the port and harbour of Aden. The old city of Crater can be seen, as its name suggests, as a lighter patch within the dark circle of an extinct volcano, at the top of the head of the 'golf-club' that makes up the Aden Peninsula. The modern city lies to the left of it, with the airport of Khormaksar a light grey bar across the peninsula. The towns of Maala and Tawahi lie below, on the left-hand side of the broad part of the peninsula, and Tawahi Harbour curves round to the peninsula of Little Aden.

Image scales and dates
Page 90: 1 cm = 5.6 km, December 1972.
Page 91: 1 cm = 3.7 km, October 1975.

89

The Falkland Islands

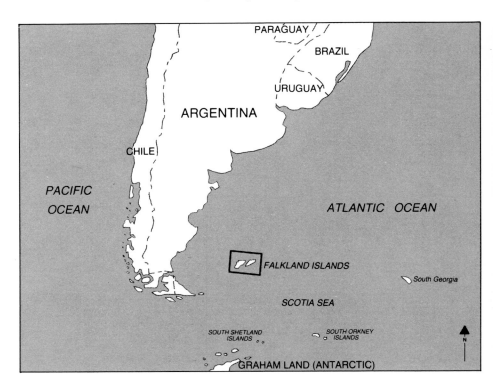

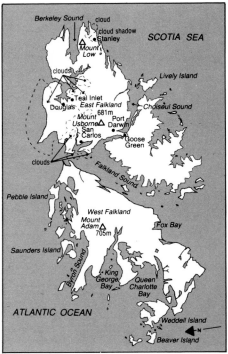

The dates of the images that make up this scene are significant. Although Landsat satellites have been operating since 1972, no one thought it worthwhile to image the Falkland Islands until ten years later. Then, on 2 April 1982, an occupation force from Argentina landed there. A British force set sail for the South Atlantic a few days later, and the islands became a centre of world attention.

The Falklands, known in Argentina as Las Islas Malvinas, lie in the South Atlantic about 480 kilometres (300 miles) away from the South American mainland. They are a group of about 200 islands, but 98 per cent of the land area is on the two main islands of East and West Falkland. Although their latitude, 52 degrees, puts them about the same distance from the equator as London, the climate more resembles that of northern Scotland, with strong winds scouring the extensive bogs and rocky outcrops. The islands are often cloud covered, and to create the present image it was necessary to piece together segments of satellite coverage obtained on three successive days, which is why the black area of water around the islands has been trimmed to its irregular shape.

The picture clearly displays the rough, geologically complex terrain and the absence of large settlements. The population of the whole islands, prior to the Argentine invasion, was less than 2,000. The landscape has not changed significantly since Charles Darwin and H.M.S. *Beagle* arrived there in 1833: 'The land is low and undulating with stony peaks and bare ridges; it is universally covered by a brown wiry grass . . . the whole landscape from the uniformity of the brown colour has an air of extreme desolation.' The principal industry is sheep farming, and the island supports about 600,000 animals. The capital is Stanley, on the east shore of East Falkland.

Most of the sites of 1982 military activity are clearly visible on this picture. The land-based fighting took place almost exclusively on East Falkland, although the first British military sortie, on 16 May, was against Argentine aircraft located on an airstrip on Pebble Island, to the left of West Falkland. The main British landing took place a week later, on 21-23 May, when 5,000 Marines established the British beachhead around San Carlos, on the upper shore of Falkland Sound. Goose Green and Port Darwin were retaken by 28 May, with the capture of 1,400 Argentine troops, and Douglas and Teal Inlet were secured on 30 May. An 80-kilometre (50-mile) march on Stanley, where the main Argentine force of about 10,000 men was located, then took place. Stanley, obscured on this scene by a dark cloud cover, was surrendered by the Argentine forces on 14 June, and shortly thereafter an Argentine garrison of 1,000 troops at Fox Bay on West Falkland also surrendered, to put an end to hostilities.

For so desolate and remote an area, the Falklands have a surprising history of international conflict. Early British settlers were expelled by Spain in 1774. Argentine settlers arrived in 1829, but were in turn expelled in 1831. A British colony has existed there since 1833, but Argentina has disputed possession for all that period, arguing its case in the United Nations since 1965.

Before the construction of the Panama Canal, the Falklands held a strategically important position with respect to travel round Cape Horn. Today, international interest may be more commercial. East of the islands, beneath the turbulent waters of the South Atlantic, lies one of the world's largest unexplored sedimentary basins, a tempting target for offshore oil and gas exploration.

Image scale and dates: 1 cm = 8.7 km, 20, 21, 22 April 1982.

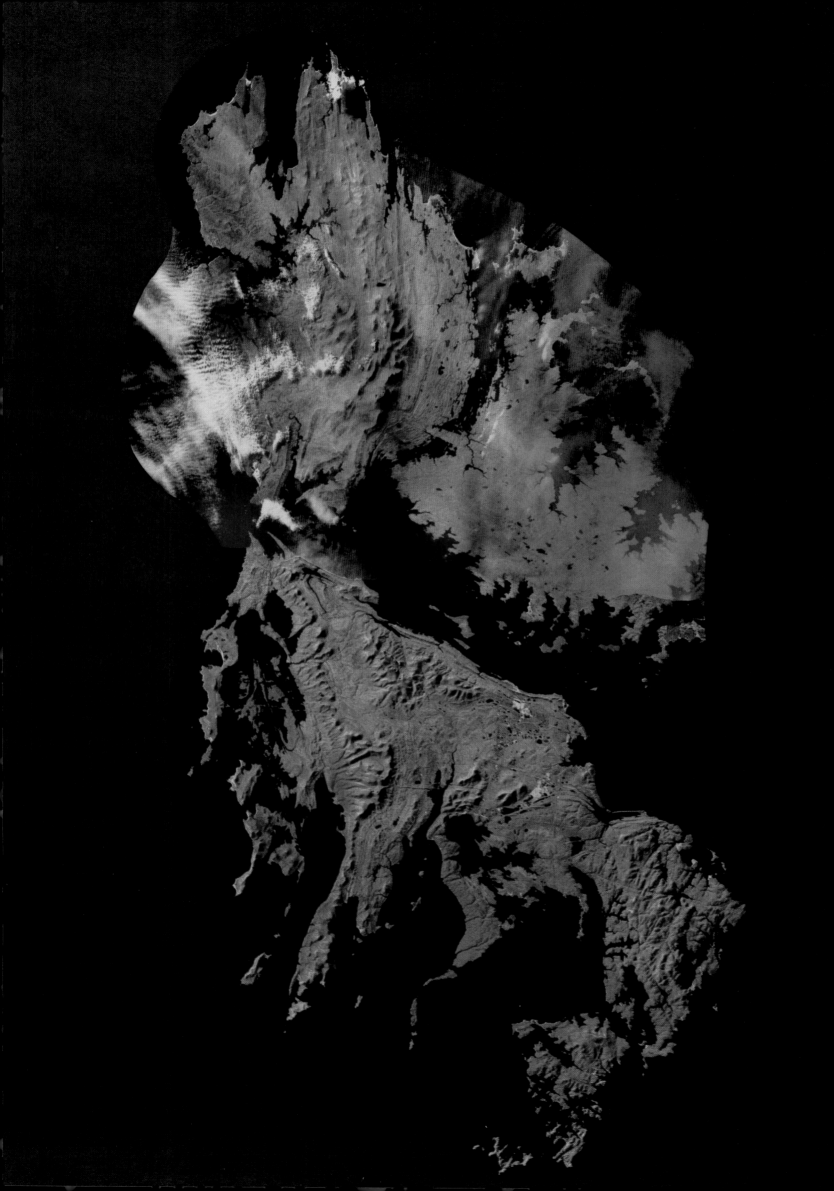

Moscow

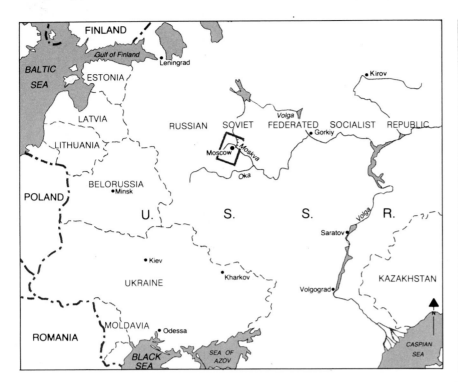

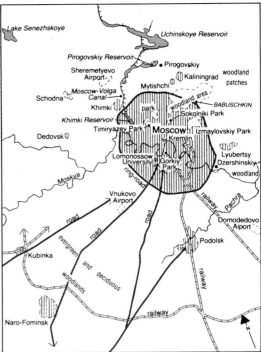

Moscow is the capital of the U.S.S.R., the most important city of Old Russia, and the political, administrative, and financial centre of the Soviet Union. Since 1917, Moscow can also claim to be the focal point of world communism. As a military and ideological power centre it is matched only by Washington, D.C. Moscow has a long history of combat. Founded in the eleventh century, it has been attacked, burned, and besieged many times: by the Tartars in 1237, 1382, 1571, and 1591; by the Poles in 1610; by Napoleon and the French Army, who held the city briefly in 1812; and finally by the Germans, who laid siege to it in 1941 but did not occupy it.

With a population of over 7 million, the city is seen here as the large blue-grey urban area to the right centre of the picture. Moscow lies squarely on the Moskva River, visible as a dark line that bisects the image area as it meanders from left to right to finally join the Oka River, beyond the right-hand edge of the scene. The Moskva River is navigable, but a better waterway for transportation is provided by the Moscow-Volga Canal, completed in 1937. It is seen here at the beginning of its 130-kilometre (80-mile) journey north to the Volga River. The line of the canal begins in the suburbs on the left side of Moscow, then passes through the Khimki, Pirogovskiy and Uchinskoye Reservoirs, the latter a long dark-blue body of water visible at the top of the image despite the haze in the upper part of the scene. Beyond the reservoirs the canal can be followed to the upper edge of the image.

Within the urban area of Moscow a number of familiar features are visible. Gorkiy Park is the thin red strip on the right bank of the river in the centre. Above it, on the other side of the river at the top left of the curve, the Kremlin appears as a small isosceles triangle. Built in the twelfth century, burned and rebuilt in the thirteenth and sixteenth, the

Kremlin is the Russian national symbol of power and government. Further up, many of Moscow's recreation areas show as patches of red, including Izmaylovskiy, Sokolniki and Timiryazev Parks, inside the Moscow ring-road. The city is built on a radial-ring pattern, but the inner two rings of roads cannot be distinguished from the general pattern of buildings. The outer ring-road is most easily seen where it passes as a blue line through vegetated parkland areas.

Beyond the ring-road the runways of Moscow's two major airports can be seen to the left of the city, Vnukovo below and Sheremetyevo above. A third major airport, Domodedovo, is clearly visible to the lower right of the picture, right of the blue-grey suburban patch of Podolsk. Other Moscow suburbs can be seen at Kaliningrad and Mytishchi, below Uchinskoye Reservoir and connected to the city through a long urban corridor; at Dedovsk, below the layer of haze to the left of the city; and at Naro-Fominsk, in the bottom left-hand corner of the image. Most of the area around the city is heavily vegetated, and the blue-grey suburbs stand out clearly against the red background.

Moscow has a typical mid-continent climate, with hot summers and cold, snowy winters. Rivers are frozen for four or five months of the year. However, despite its reputation for a harsh climate (winter average temperature, −9 degrees Centigrade, 15 Fahrenheit), the Moscow area was formerly covered with dense evergreen and deciduous forest.
Today, large patches of woodland still show dark brownish-red across the image, between the lighter colour of planted fields. The principal crops are the ones traditionally associated with Russian life: oats, rye, and flax.

Image scale and date: 1 cm = 3.9 km, May 1975.

The Suez Canal

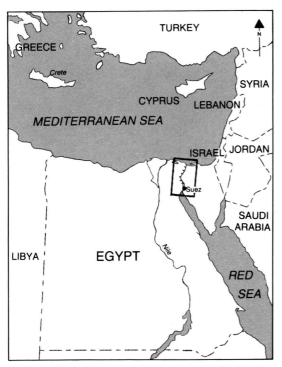

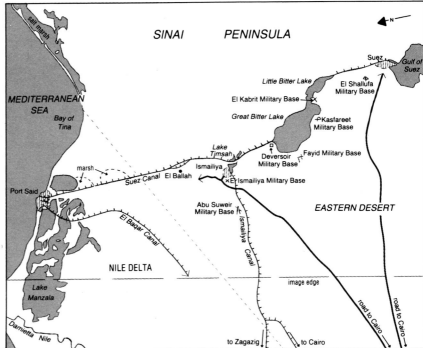

The early sea routes from Europe to India and China required long and difficult voyages round the whole of Africa. To many merchants, especially those from the eastern Mediterranean, an 'interior sea journey' across the narrow tongue of land between the Mediterranean Sea and the Red Sea must have seemed very attractive. That journey was finally made possible in the middle of the last century, when the Frenchman Ferdinand de Lesseps organized and led the construction of the Suez Canal.

The canal is shown on the image overleaf in its entire length, from the head of the Gulf of Suez to Port Said on the Mediterranean. The narrow line of the canal is clearly visible as it starts from Suez across to the Little Bitter Lake (Buheirat-Murrat-el-Sughra) and the Great Bitter Lake (Buheirat-Murrat-el-Kubra), then on through another straight section to the salt-water lagoon of Lake Timsah, just above Ismailiya. Continuing further to the left, the canal divides for a few miles at El Ballah above the Firdan swing bridge (not visible), then reunites to form a single channel all the way to Port Said. At Ismailiya, the freshwater Ismailiya Canal (Tirat el Ismailiya) is seen as a thin black line running down from Lake Timsah at the left of a long tentacle of irrigated red vegetation towards Cairo and the Nile Delta. The Ismailiya Canal's completion by de Lesseps in 1862 came a few years before the main canal's official opening in November 1869.

The Suez Canal runs its course between the light tan sand dunes of the Sinai Peninsula, some of them up to 90 metres (300 feet) high, and the bright dry wadis of the Egyptian Eastern (Arabian) Desert. In the lower left of the image is part of Lake Manzala, the salty, grey-blue body of water between Port Said and the Nile Delta. The black patch above Port Said

by the sea is a lake, with dark brown patches of seasonal marshland to the right, further inland. The bright white areas are flat sand with a high content of dried salt. Forming the coast is a narrow sandbar which stretches from above Port Said past the curving Bay of Tina and on to the shoreline salt marshes of the Sinai Peninsula at the upper left of the image.

There are seven military bases within the image area (see map) and a number of airstrips are visible on the picture. The prominent one on the lower shore of the Great Bitter Lake belongs to the Fayid Military Base, and the one on the left of the Ismailiya Canal, close to the point where the thin dark line of the road to Cairo heads down to the right across the desert, is Abu Suweir Military Base.

The extraordinary strategic importance of the Suez Canal was recognized even before it was completed in its modern form (the first channel connecting the Gulf of Suez to the Nile via the Bitter Lakes was dug long ago, in 2000 B.C.). Capable of handling ships of up to 10.5 metres (35 feet) draft, the canal carried over 115 million net tonnes of shipping in 1955, including 67 million tonnes of crude oil from the Middle East to Europe. In 1956 the seizing of the canal by Egypt (which hoped to use revenues from it to finance the construction of the Aswan High Dam) created a major international crisis. Soon afterwards traffic was blocked by debris and sunken ships. The canal was re-opened in April 1957, then closed again by the Arab-Israeli War of 1967. After eight more years it was finally cleared of sunken debris and re-opened in 1975. However, the uncertainty of its future and the increasing use of other forms of transport make it unlikely that the canal will regain its former prominence in Middle East and world affairs.

Image scale and date: 1 cm = 3.7 km, May 1978.

The English Channel

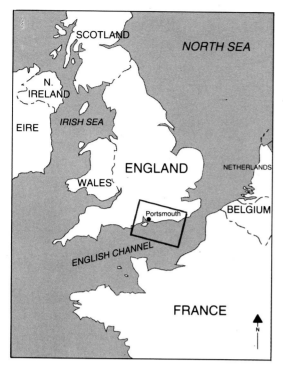

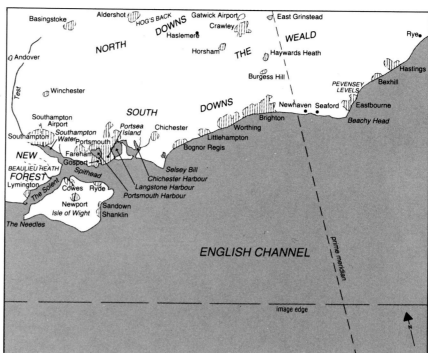

The English Channel has been for centuries the principal highway and barrier between England and the Continent. The full stretch from Lymington to Rye is displayed with unusual clarity on the haze-free and almost cloud-free summer image reproduced on pages 100-1.

Every town of significance along the coastline is visible. Beginning on the left, Lymington is seen as a bluish area on the Solent, with the spit of land carrying Hurst Castle just below it. The light hexagonal pattern of the disused airport on the dark oval of the lower part of Beaulieu Heath is clearly visible to the north. Beyond the broad entrance to Southampton Water lies Southampton, England's premier passenger port. The River Test can be traced north from Southampton by following the red line of vegetation bordering the river valley. The blue-white strip of Southampton Airport is visible just above the city.

East of Southampton Water lie Spithead and the unmistakeable indentations of Portsmouth, Langstone, and Chichester harbours. These inlets, like Southampton Water, were formed as river valleys long ago, during the last Ice Age, and later drowned by the sea. Today they provide excellent deep-water access. Whereas Southampton is a passenger and freight port, Portsmouth has long served as one of Britain's main naval bases and garrisons. Most of the naval station and arsenal occupies the south-west part of Portsea Island, with submarine yards at Gosport. The main city of Portsmouth can be seen between Portsmouth and Langstone harbours. The white line of the M27 motorway is clearly visible, connecting Portsmouth and Southampton. Proceeding further east we see the characteristic promontory of Selsey Bill, and beyond it along the coast Bognor Regis, Littlehampton, Worthing, Brighton, Newhaven and Seaford before we come to the 150-metre (500-foot) chalk cliffs of Beachy Head. Beyond this, Eastbourne, Bexhill and Hastings can be seen, and at the right-hand edge of the image lies Rye.

Offshore lies the unmistakeable shape of the Isle of Wight. In addition to its main towns of Newport, Cowes, Ryde, Sandown and Shanklin, the line of the long chalk ridge that forms the backbone of the island can be traced all the way from The Needles in the west to the steep edge of Culver Cliff above Sandown in the east.

Inland, the image reveals much of the structure of south-east England. The edge of the New Forest, preserved by royal decree since Norman times, lies as a dark-red triangle to the left of Southampton. Further east, the north-facing scarp of the chalky South Downs can be seen as a distinct line running from north of Portsmouth to its eastern terminus at Beachy Head. Beyond it to the north lie the clay lands of The Weald, a broad strip, wooded until the sixteenth century, that now stretches as cattle pasture and orchards all the way to the low-lying marshlands above Hastings. The marshes of Pevensey Levels stand out as a bright red patch above Eastbourne. Further north, near the top of the image area, from left to right Basingstoke, Aldershot, Crawley and above it Gatwick Airport are visible as blue urban areas.

Image scale and date: 1 cm = 3.7 km, July 1975.

The Strait of Gibraltar

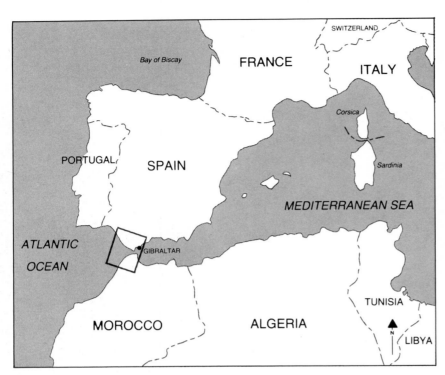

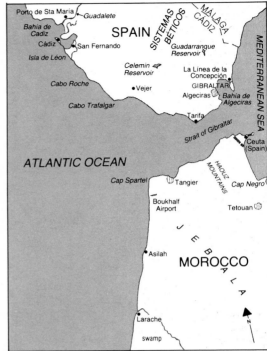

Europe and Africa reach their point of closest approach here at the western end of the Mediterranean Sea. Thirteen kilometres (8 miles) across at its narrowest, the Strait of Gibraltar has been of unique strategic importance for hundreds of years, as a key corridor on the sea-road from North Europe to Italy, Greece, Africa and the Middle East.

The Rock of Gibraltar, a U.K. Dependent Territory since 1713, stands at the north-east end of the Strait. It is seen here as a southward-jutting sharp peninsula, ending at Europa Point and connected at the other end to the Spanish mainland by a low-lying sandy spit of land only 3 metres (10 feet) above sea-level. The limestone mass of the Rock, rising to almost 430 metres (1,400 feet), can be seen as the dark backbone of the peninsula. The Spanish town of La Línea de la Concepción lies beyond it, to the north. The moles and jetties of Gibraltar Harbour are visible in the west, projecting into the Bahía de Algeciras, with the town of Algeciras showing as a blue patch on the western shore. Gibraltar's airport is a blue horizontal line across the northern end of the Rock.

The upper section of the picture lies almost completely in the southern Spanish province of Cádiz. The city of Cádiz can be seen to the north-west, built on the rocky end of the narrow, sandy spit that borders the Bahía de Cádiz. The outer bay, with the Guadalete estuary visible on its shore, has 12-18 metres (40-60 feet) of water and can accommodate the largest freighters; the inner bay shows a lighter blue, indicating its shallower channels. On the Isla de Léon, south of Cádiz, lies the light-blue patch of San Fernando, the naval base and arsenal. The white-flecked dark blue to the right of this is a series of salt pans. The mottled white, blue and red area that

stretches inland from Cádiz down past Cabo Trafalgar to the southern tip of Tarifa and extends east as far as the dark-red wooded slopes of the southern Sistemas Béticos, covered with cork oak and pines, is part of the fertile plain of Sevilla. It produces grapes, olives and other fruit.

South of the Strait lies Morocco, with a small area belonging to Spain at the end of the peninsula in the north-east. The Spanish town of Ceuta shows at the tip of the peninsula, to the right of the red Haouz Mountains. South of Ceuta the town of Tetouan is visible lying just below Cap Negro. Tangier, the famous international zone of the 1930s and 1940s before it became part of Morocco in 1956, shows as the blue patch on the north-west shore, east of Cap Spartel. The Atlantic coast of Morocco is seen as a dry, blue-grey area down past Asilah, until the land south of Larache below the faintly visible river shows the reds and greens of swamp.

Two of the most striking features of this image do not lie on the land areas. To the west, out in the Atlantic Ocean, the edge of a great circular cloud pattern can be seen − an anticyclone. And east, beyond the Strait itself, where Atlantic waters are moving into the Mediterranean, a complex spreading pattern of waves is visible. This is caused by compression and rarefaction of the surface water layers induced by the flow past the narrow strait, which slightly changes the strength of reflected sunlight received at the satellite.

The dark lines with red dots on their left which are visible in the Atlantic to the right of the anticyclone and in the Strait of Gibraltar just above the middle of the Moroccan coast are not physical features, they are lines of dropped data.

Image scale and date: 1 cm = 5.8 km, July 1979.

Taiwan

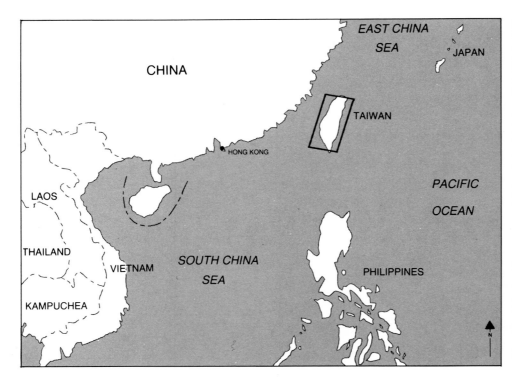

The island of Taiwan lies south-east of mainland China, across the 130-kilometre (80-mile) wide Formosa Strait. Since 1949, when the Kuomintang Government moved there after defeat on the Chinese mainland, Taiwan has been the seat of government and principal land base of the Nationalist Republic of China. Ownership of the island is a cause of great tension in south-east Asia. Both the Nationalist Republic of China and the mainland People's Republic of China make militant claims to the territory, creating an uneasy stalemate that has continued for over thirty years.

Taiwan is 380 kilometres (235 miles) long and 145 kilometres (90 miles) wide. Almost the whole island is visible on this mosaic of two Landsat scenes, with the exception of the southern tip and of a small area north of Tai-pei, the capital city of 2 million people.

Warmed by the Black, or Tsushima, Current, Taiwan enjoys a mild climate and productive agriculture. The general structure of the island is clearly visible on this picture. The Chung-yang Mountains run north-south like a long backbone, seen here as red forested peaks capped by white clouds. The range rises to nearly 4,000 metres (13,000 feet), with conifer cover above 2,700 metres (9,000 feet), and mixed stands of cypress, cedar, juniper and maple down to 1,800 metres (6,000 feet). Bamboos and palms cover the lower slopes.

East of the Chung-yang is a narrow valley, created by a geological fault and running from Hua-lien to Tai-tung in the south. It is seen as a blue strip on the image. The fall-off from the mountains both east and west of the valley is steep, and there is limited agriculture here and on the infertile high ground. The island's main agricultural production is provided by a broad alluvial plain west of the Chung-yang Mountains. Seen here as a pale-pink area that runs

from Tai-pei to south of Ping-tung, the plain is crossed by the wide blue strips of numerous rivers, heavily laden with sediment, their deeper channels visible as dark lines within the strips. The carried sediments create the noticeable offshore rim of hazy blue along the western shore of the island. The principal crop here is paddy rice, followed in importance by sugar cane in the south-west, then sweet potatoes, tea, peanuts, bananas, and pineapples. Most fields permit two crops per year. Animal protein is provided by numerous pig farms, by offshore fishing, and by fish ponds. The latter are visible as innumerable dark-blue pinpricks in the pink plain south-west of Tai-pei, and in the extensive pattern of fish pens and ponds along the lower west side of the image.

Energy for the island is provided mainly by an extensive hydro-electric grid, with its centre at Sunmoon Lake. The lake is visible here as a small patch of dark blue in the Chung-yang Mountains, close to the centre of the image. The electric grid feeds energy to the towns on the west coast, particularly Tai-pei, which have thriving manufacturing industries.

The strong mixture of Chinese and Japanese influences throughout Taiwan agriculture, land use, and industry is no accident. The island was a base for pirates from both countries in the fifteenth century and then became a home for Chinese immigrants in about 1700 following unsuccessful attempts by the Dutch and Spanish to create colonies there. In 1895 it was ceded to Japan after the Sino-Japanese war and became a major staging area for Japanese operations in Indonesia during the Second World War. It was finally turned back to the Chinese Nationalists in 1945 but retains much of the Japanese education system and lifestyle.

Image scale and date: 1 cm = 11.6 km, November 1972.

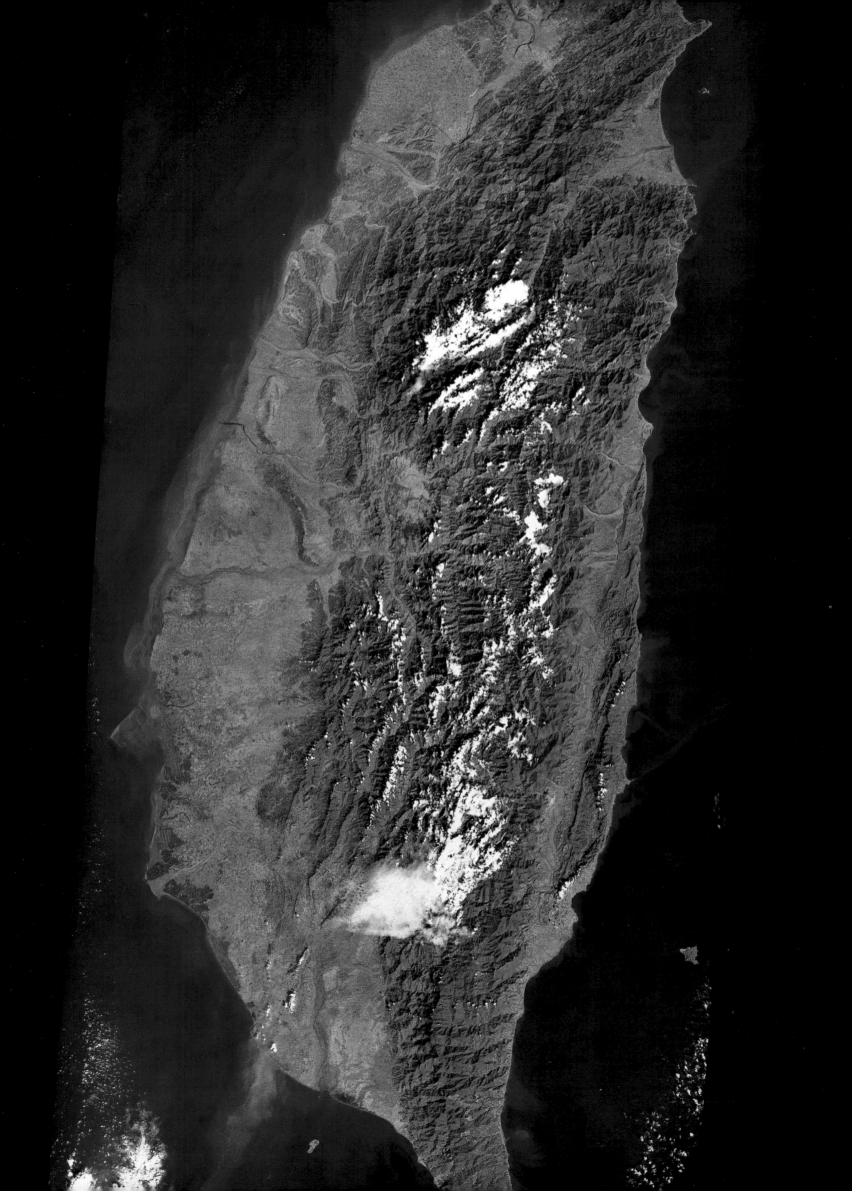

Los Alamos, New Mexico

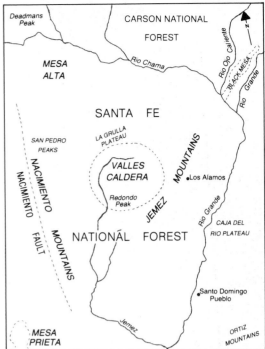

This scene lies in northern New Mexico, near the border with Colorado. Albuquerque is 32 kilometres (20 miles) south, and Sante Fe a few kilometres south-east. This is high, dry country, with every part of the image more than 1.5 kilometres above sea-level. Vegetation shows as a dark-red ground cover only in the river valleys and on the cooler and damper mountain slopes. Pine, fir, and spruce occupy the higher regions, with cedar on the lower hills. The lowest plateaux appear on this scene as an almost bare grey-white, supporting only tough grasses and occasional trees. New Mexico was the former home of many American Indian tribes, notably the Navajos, Apaches, and a number of Pueblo-dwellers, and today this area has many Indian reservations.

The striking oval feature at image centre is the Valles Caldera, a huge extinct volcanic crater nearly 24 kilometres (15 miles) across. It was formed in a catastrophic explosion about a million years ago, and later upwellings of lava can be seen as the smaller cones and domes at the northern edge of the crater. In the southern centre of the crater is Redondo Peak, a snow-capped mountain rising to 3,430 metres (11,250 feet). Snow cover is also visible above 2,700 metres (9,000 feet) on the high La Grulla Plateau to the north, and in the San Pedro Peaks at the western edge of the image. A few miles east of the Valles Caldera the town of Los Alamos shows as a small patch of grey on wooded mountain slopes.

The irrigated valley of the Rio Grande runs along the eastern side of the image. North-east of the Valles Caldera it branches, with the line of the Rio Grande leading north towards its source in Colorado, and the Rio Chama curling its way round to the north of the great caldera. The Rio Grande follows the line of a rift valley, broadening at the southern boundary of the scene to become a fertile agricultural area near Albuquerque (beyond the image area). To the right of the Rio Grande, at the lower corner of the image, the Ortiz Mountains show as a darker patch, while at the lower left the dark lava-capped plateau of Mesa Prieta can be seen. North of the Mesa Prieta the long, straight Nacimiento Fault is visible, forming a sharp line between the dry plateau to the west and the wooded Nacimiento Mountains to the east. Most of the red woodlands seen on this picture form part of the Santa Fe National Forest, stretching up to meet the light-red Carson National Forest at the north-east corner of the image.

In the past quarter century the population of New Mexico has grown rapidly, as part of the booming 'Sun Belt' of the United States. Forty years ago, however, the region was almost deserted. It was ideal as the location for a project that called for wartime isolation and total secrecy. In November 1942 Los Alamos was chosen as the chief site for the Manhattan Project, and in March 1943 the first group of scientists moved in. At that remote and lonely location, on the eastern flank of the Valles Caldera, the world's first atomic bomb was designed and built between 1943 and 1945.

Image scale and date: 1 cm = 3.9 km, November 1974.

Alamogordo, New Mexico

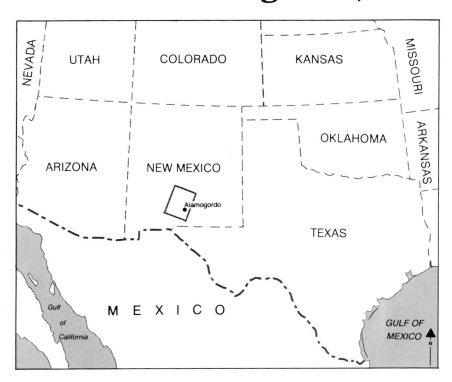

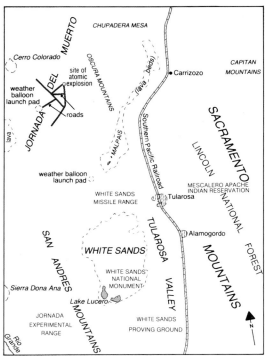

This scene is 160 kilometres (100 miles) south of the previous image, only 80 kilometres (50 miles) north of the U.S.-Mexico border.

The most striking feature of this picture is the large white patch in the centre, contrasting with the curving black strip further north. The light patch is White Sands, a flat, alkaline, gypsum-covered area 32 kilometres (20 miles) across from north to south that strongly reflects sunlight. The material was blown there from the weathering of exposed beds of rock in the San Andres Mountains, seen just to the west as a rugged line of brown. At the south-west end of White Sands is the drying playa of Lake Lucero which shows as blue. It is the only body of water visible on this image. The blue flecks higher up are drying briny areas, and this dampness is the main reason for the darker beige tones on the left-hand side of the alkali flat. What appears to be a large dark lake in the centre of the top half of the image is the Malpais, a bed of black lava that vented from the earth in the north and spread 60 kilometres (40 miles) down towards White Sands.

West of the San Andres Mountains, and stretching from roughly the middle of the scene to the Chupadera Mesa at its upper boundary, is the Jornada del Muerto, the 'Journey of the Dead Man'. This is a 160-kilometre (100-mile) stretch of waterless sand and rocks, well known to and avoided by early travellers through the American West. At the western edge of the picture, within the Jornada del Muerto, part of another dark lava bed can be seen.

The right-hand side of the image shows the brownish-red of the Sacramento Mountains, preserved as the Lincoln National Forest and the Mescalero Apache Indian Reservation. The dark line of the Southern Pacific Railroad is visible west of the mountains, passing through the towns of Tularosa and Alamogordo and on up to the top of the image. At the upper edge of the forest is the prominent east-west ridge of the Capitan Mountains, to the right of the northern end of the Malpais.

The names through this whole area confirm its unpleasant reputation with western travellers: apart from the Journey of the Dead Man and the Malpais ('Badlands'), the names of the canyons that cut west into the San Andres Mountains tell their own tale — Ash Canyon, Lost Man Canyon, Sulphur Canyon, Howinahell Canyon, and Dead Man Canyon.

Today the area has other associations. The White Sands Proving Ground and White Sands Missile Range near the image centre were America's first facilities for the testing of large rockets. Now this area is an alternative landing site for the Space Shuttle, and the two large, tan circles visible in the upper left of the image are gypsum-covered launch pads for weather balloons. The Jornada Experimental Range lies lower down, on the west flank of the San Andres Mountains.

To most people, however, the principal association of this image area is with the events that took place here in 1945. In that year, at 5.30 a.m. on 16 July, the world's first atomic bomb was successfully tested at Trinity Site, in the Jornada del Muerto. The bomb was exploded at the top of a 50-metre (160-foot) water-tower, at latitude 33 40' 31" N, longitude 106 28' 29" W, to the west of the Oscura Mountains in the upper left quadrant of the image. The scar of the explosion and subsequent ground disturbance can be seen as a small dark spot, about 2 centimetres north-east of the upper weather balloon launch pad, and 1 centimetre west of the broken line of the mountain ridge. Faint roads are visible running south, south-west and north from the centre point of the explosion.

Image scale and date: 1 cm = 5.6 km, November 1972.

Hiroshima

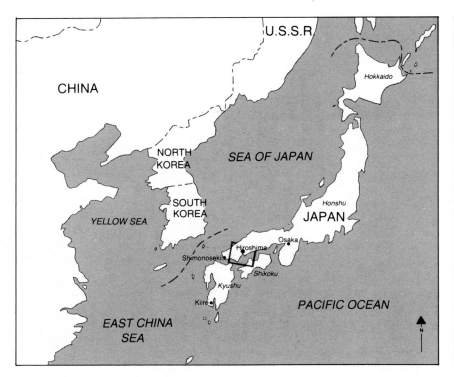

Japan's Inland Sea, the Seto Naikai, or 'sea without straits', is a shallow, placid body of water that runs 420 kilometres (260 miles) from Osaka in the east to Shimonoseki in the west (both off the image). It is bounded in the north by Honshu Island, in the south by Shikoku Island, and in the west by Kyushu Island, which is off the image area. The Inland Sea is packed with small islands of every size, and this image of a central portion of the sea shows several dozen of them.

Shikoku Island, in the upper right quadrant of the image, is the smallest (18,800 square kilometres; 7,250 square miles), of Japan's four major land masses, and most of its population lives along the coast of the Inland Sea. Matsuyama, Shikoku's largest city (350,000 people), is seen here on the lower coast, as a blue patch within the light-pink background of the fertile Dogo Plain. The principal crops are rice and citrus fruits, and the city also enjoys a large tourist trade. The only other city of significance visible on Shikoku is Niihama, seen on the coast at the top edge of the picture.

The Honshu side of the sea is much more developed. A shoreline 'industrial belt' extends from Osaka to the western Shimonoseki Strait, both of which are beyond the image area. Numerous blue patches of urban development can be seen on this picture, all the way from Fukuyama (160,000 people) to Tokuyama (90,000 people) in the bottom right. The latter city has a thriving petrochemicals industry, and the islands just offshore are a national source of granite. Round the cape above Tokuyama lies Iwakuni, a factory town of about 100,000 people, and directly across Hiroshima

Bay from Iwakuni is Kure. Once the naval base for the Japanese fleet, Kure has four excellent harbours that are now used in its shipbuilding activities. The Kure shipyard constructs the world's largest ships, supertankers that carry up to 500,000 tonnes, are over 400 metres (0.25 miles) long, and draw nearly 30 metres (100 feet) of water. Loaded, these vessels are too deep to enter the Inland Sea and discharge at the port of Kiire, off the image, on the western island of Kyushu. Inland from Kure about 30 kilometres (20 miles) the small blue patch of Saijo can be seen, famous throughout Japan for its special brands of sake.

To the left of Hiroshima Bay lies the city of Hiroshima, capital of the Hiroshima prefecture and at 800,000 people this scene's biggest city. It stands on the delta of the Ota River, which flows down to the sea from the Chugoku Mountains. The division of the city into five finger-like delta islands is clear on the image.

The city is old and has a long history, but to most people it is indelibly linked with a single event. On the morning of 6 August 1945 a B-29 bomber, the *Enola Gay*, flew over Hiroshima and dropped an atomic bomb. Targeted for the Aioi Bridge in the centre of the city, the bomb exploded at 8.15 a.m., at a height of about 600 metres (2,000 feet). An accurate count of the dead has never been possible, but estimates range from 63,000 to 240,000.

Ground zero for the first atomic bomb used in war is now the site of a Peace Memorial Park. It is not visible on this image.

Image scale and date: 1 cm = 5.3 km, September 1979.

Food and Fibre

The direction of agricultural development for the remainder of this century can be discerned from a few simple facts: prior to 1930, only Western Europe imported grain; all other areas of the world were either exporters or self-sufficient; before 1950, the increases in available food supply came from increases in both planted acreage and yield per acre, but since 1950, acreage has remained almost constant, and increases have come only from use of more fertilizers, improved crops, and better production methods; until 1961, the developing world produced on balance a total food surplus; since 1961, the developing world has suffered an overall food shortage.

These changes largely reflect the population growth pattern described earlier in the section on the Ancient World. Food production has certainly increased, and sometimes spectacularly, as when new hybrid grains were introduced during the 1960s. Unfortunately, these gains have been more than balanced by the additional 2,000 million people who have appeared on earth since 1950 — 200,000 new mouths to be fed in the world every day. An estimated 500,000,000 people are now classified by the Population Reference Bureau as 'severely malnourished'. Fifteen to twenty million people die each year of hunger. Yet less than 10 per cent of the world's land surface is used for agriculture.

To set this in perspective and to see what solutions there may be to the problem of inadequate food supplies, it is necessary to look at the global distribution of land use. Of the world total of 148.9 million square kilometres (57.5 million square miles) of land area, roughly 20 per cent is too cold to support agriculture, another 20 per cent is too arid, 20 per cent is too mountainous, and about 14 per cent has infertile soils. This leaves 26 per cent, or almost 40 million square kilometres (15 million square miles), available for the cultivation of food and fibre — yet only 13 million of these are cultivated. There would seem to be ample opportunity to increase planted acreages and total world food, and to provide the additional 50 per cent production increase that will be needed by the year 2000, just to hold per capita food supply at its present level.

Unfortunately, there are other limitations. If tropical forests are cleared and planted, the soils usually prove to be leached of minerals and poor in productivity; and unless strict soil conservation measures are followed, topsoil is lost in just a few years. The same problem occurs in dry prairies, with the added problem that irrigation is needed for regular crop production. In many cases, the clearing and planting of new lands has been shortly followed by the development of dust bowls, loss of soils, and desertification (in 1934, a single storm removed an estimated 300,000,000 tonnes of topsoils from the U.S. prairies).

Space observations are an ideal tool to monitor changes of this type. With new Landsat images available in cloud-free areas every eighteen days, a simple computer processing technique will permit the direct calculation and evaluation of changes from one month to the next. Distinguishing vegetated from non-vegetated areas is one of the simplest and most reliable uses of infra-red imagery, and sand and salt encroachment, decline in soil fertility, and loss of crop vigour can all be monitored quickly and inexpensively.

This space technology certainly will not solve the problem of feeding the world. No single activity will do that; however, data derived from space will allow us to measure the problem, and to assess the value of different and innovative agricultural practices.

Sudan Irrigation Scheme

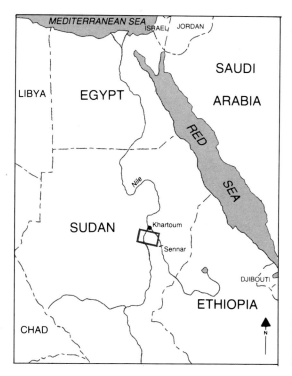

Sudan is Africa's largest country, over 2,500,000 square kilometres (nearly 1,000,000 square miles) that extend from Egypt in the north to Uganda and Zaire in the south. It is mainly composed of great level plains of clay and sand, with a climate that ranges from northern desert through savanna to tropical jungle at its southern border. Despite its great size and moderate population (18 million), Sudan is one of the world's poorer countries, relying on its agriculture to provide both domestic food and most exports.

The River Nile runs the entire length of the country, and for many centuries the Sudanese have relied upon its waters to irrigate their fields. Sixty kilometres (40 miles) north of the image area reproduced overleaf, the Blue Nile and the White Nile meet at Khartoum (see pages 138-9). At the centre of this scene lies the fertile triangle of El Gezira (El Jazira), the location of one of the world's most successful projects for river control and irrigation.

The natural rainfall of the area is only about 30 centimetres (12 inches) a year, and it occurs all in the summer months. This is too little for the growth of rain-fed crops. The vegetation of the beige desert visible to the west of the White Nile is tough grasses and thorny shrubs, including gum arabic (acacia gum), whose sticky resin is useful in printing, in food preparation, and in making emulsions and cosmetics. It is one of the country's few natural exports. The grey-blue land to the east of the White Nile holds more moisture and is a slightly more fertile area of heavy clay.

Without irrigation the natural surface cover of El Gezira is that visible in the lower right of the scene: sandy dunes and clays, with little vegetation. The soil is not good, and even within the irrigated area bare intrusions of infertile dunes persist. Agriculture for many centuries has therefore relied on the annual flooding of the Nile, but this too has disadvantages. The level of the rivers, particularly the Blue Nile, is very variable. At flood times, the quantity of water descending the Blue Nile is sixty times its lowest volume, occasionally peaking to 300 times, and most of this would run off to the north before it could be harnessed for crop irrigation. In the early 1900s the Gezira Scheme was proposed: a dam would be built on the Blue Nile at Sennar, south-east of the scene area, to control the Nile and allow its waters to be diverted over the flat plain of El Gezira for systematic irrigation. The dam was finally built in 1925, and a great network of canals dug in the stoneless soil. In El Gezira and in the later southern Manaqil Extension (completed in 1962) over 16,000 kilometres (10,000 miles) of canals now irrigate the neat pattern of fields. Only the largest of them can be seen on the image, but field boundaries follow the canal lines.

The striking field pattern visible here is a consequence of the farming practices used in the area. There are two main crops, long-staple cotton and millet. These are rotated on a regular basis, with roughly half the land lying fallow at any given time. This creates the red (cropped) and grey-blue (fallow) patterns of rectangles seen on the image. To the south, a large area of infertile sands and clays stands out within the agricultural pattern.

The land bordering the broad dark-blue strip of the White Nile, on the left of the picture, is fed by pumped water rather than the gravity feed of the canals, and in addition to the two principal crops of cotton and millet the area produces *durra* (a form of sorghum wheat), sesame, rice, peanuts, coffee, sugar cane, and tobacco.

Image scale and date: 1 cm = 3.7 km, December 1979.

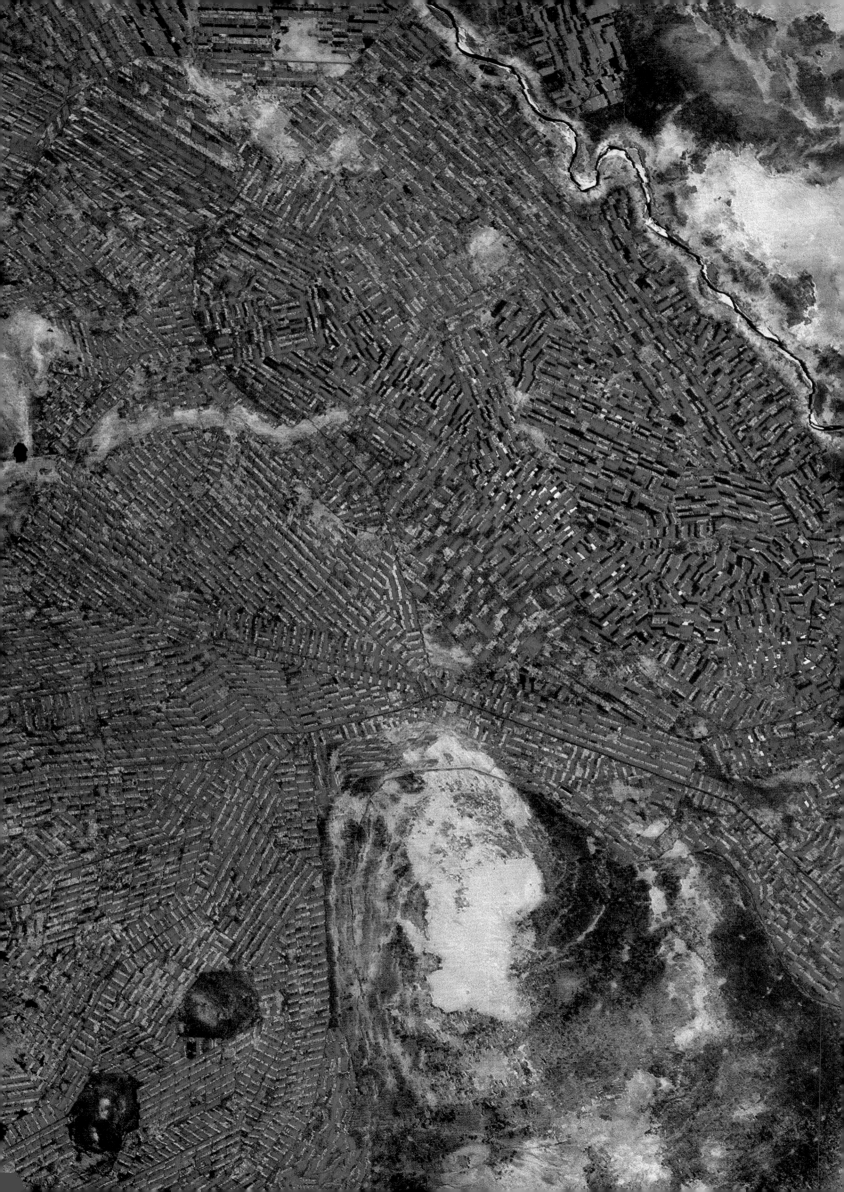

Mennonite Colony in Western Paraguay

Paraguay is South America's seventh largest country, with 407,000 square kilometres (157,000 square miles) of land. In the east there are fertile plains, cool highlands, forests, an abundance of hydro-electric power, and a pleasant climate; but to the west lies the Gran Chaco, part of which is covered by this image.

The Chaco is a flat, hot, insect-infested region of 155,000 square kilometres (60,000 square miles), with little water, salty wells, droughts and floods by turns, and poor drainage. Even the native Guarani Indians prefer to avoid it completely. Of Paraguay's population of 3 million, less than 110,000 live in the Chaco, sometimes termed the Chaco Boreal at this point. The Gran Chaco as a whole extends the length of Paraguay north to south and continues down into Argentina for about 700 kilometres (400 miles). It is surprising, then, to see on this Landsat image of the Chaco of western Paraguay vast evidence of ground-clearing, planting, and crop production. The explanation lies in Europe, and dates back many years.

The Mennonites are a pacifist Christian sect who originated in Switzerland in the early sixteenth century. Groups from all over Europe, following severe persecution by both Catholics and Protestants for their rejection of civil systems, emigrated to Canada, the United States, Russia, and Mexico before a large number of Mennonite colonists finally came to Paraguay early this century, mainly from Canada and later from Russia. After negotiation the Government of Paraguay agreed to allow the colonists to occupy a 132,000-hectare (325,000-acre) tract of land – but in the wilderness of the Chaco, rather than in fertile eastern Paraguay. The settlement was established in 1926, around the small town of Filadelfia and not far from the Argentine border. The image shown here displays the result of forty years of hard work.

The area frequently suffers from droughts. The natural ground cover is rough grasses, cacti, and native bushes resembling mesquite, all mixed in with swamp. There are a few species of trees unique to the Chaco, of which the most useful are the common *caranday* palm, or black palm, which produces wax, straw, and timber, and the *palo santo* tree, from which the Mennonites distil an oil used in medicines. On the cleared lands the colonists plant crops that are resistant to drought: cotton, sorghum, and castor beans. When the water supply permits, they also grow peanuts, quick to mature and harvest. The agriculture and cattle ranges are carried through on a large scale, with many of the fields visible on this image more than 1.5 kilometres square. The cleared lands are prominent as square white and greenish-white patches in the upper right quadrant, with the most recently cleared areas showing the lightest colours. The process is still going on, as the uncleared red areas within the many field boundaries indicate. Service roads running north-south and east-west can be seen as a fine network of thin white lines over most of the image.

One other curious feature of this picture is worth noting. The right side of the image has a few specks of cloud on it. Landsat always views the earth at the same local time of day, about 9.30 a.m., so south of the equator shadows should usually lie to the south-west; but the black cloud shadows here lie exactly west of the corresponding clouds. A look at the location and the date tells us why. The scene was recorded in December, and lies at latitude 23 degrees. Thus we are close to winter solstice and almost on the Tropic of Capricorn. At this location and time the sun will stand directly overhead at noon, and during the day will proceed across the sky from due east to due west, casting only east-west shadows.

Image scale and date: 1 cm = 5.2 km, December 1977.

Clear-cutting in Western Alberta

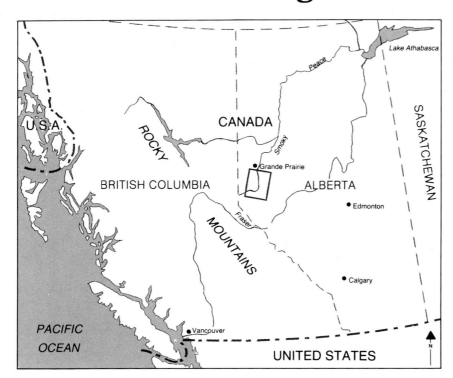 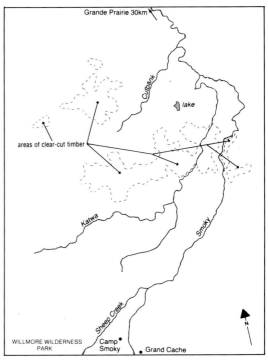

Canada is the world's second largest country in land area, exceeded only by the Soviet Union, and it has huge natural resources. That so many of these remain untapped is largely a consequence of Canada's small population – only 23 million people, in an area of 9.98 million square kilometres (3.85 million square miles), slightly larger than the whole of Europe.

This image is set in western Alberta, on the eastern flank of the Rocky Mountains. Edmonton, the capital and centre of the province's huge oil industry, lies 320 kilometres (200 miles) east. The border with British Columbia, following the continental divide of the Rocky Mountains, is a few miles west of the lower left-hand corner of the scene. The biggest town on the image is Grande Cache, population 4,500, at the bottom of the picture (not visible). Grande Prairie (population 25,000) is about 30 kilometres (20 miles) north of the scene area. At the southern edge of the picture lies the northern border of Willmore Wilderness Provincial Park, and beyond it (about 48 kilometres (30 miles) off the image) the Jasper National Park, along the crest of the Rockies. Although Alberta's population now exceeds 1.5 million, this is still a thinly populated frontier country whose natural resources have hardly begun to be exploited.

The south-west quadrant of the image shows the foothills of the Rockies, still partly snow-covered in this July scene (we are at 54 degrees north). This whole area of the mountains has extensive Cretaceous Age coal deposits, and the Smoky River, which can be seen as a thin blue line as it runs from the lower image centre north along the right-hand side of the picture, was named from the coal beds that lay along its banks. Near the top of the image the Smoky River merges with the Kakwa and Cutbank rivers, and flows on to meet the Peace River off the image area to the north. Since the Rocky Mountains provide a barrier to the west, all rivers in this part of Canada flow north and east, and the final outlet for this whole Alberta river system is in the Mackenzie Delta, 1,900 kilometres (1,200 miles) away to the north on the Beaufort Sea.

The lower plains around Grande Prairie to the north permit extensive agriculture, but throughout most of the image area there is higher ground, which ranges from 760 metres (2,500 feet) at the top of the picture to 2,400 metres (8,000 feet) at the bottom left and supports a natural wooded cover. The distinctive patchwork-quilt pattern of pinks, light green and dark green comes from clear-cutting of the woodlands, mainly consisting in this region of spruce, lodge-pole pine, Douglas fir, poplar, balsam, white birch, and tamarack. Although power tools have now replaced the traditional axe and handsaw felling methods, each July the Canadian National Logging Competition is still held at Grande Prairie. Forest roads to transport the cut timber can be seen as fine white lines running across the upper half of the image. The black patch upper centre is a lake.

As might be expected of a region that is still largely untouched by man, the area is also a haven for endangered species. It is a nesting-ground for the trumpeter swans, North America's largest wildfowl. Half a century ago the total estimated population was down to sixty-nine birds and extinction seemed certain, but with conservation and protection here and in other wilderness areas, the census has now risen to several thousand.

Image scale and date: 1 cm = 3.7 km, July 1979.

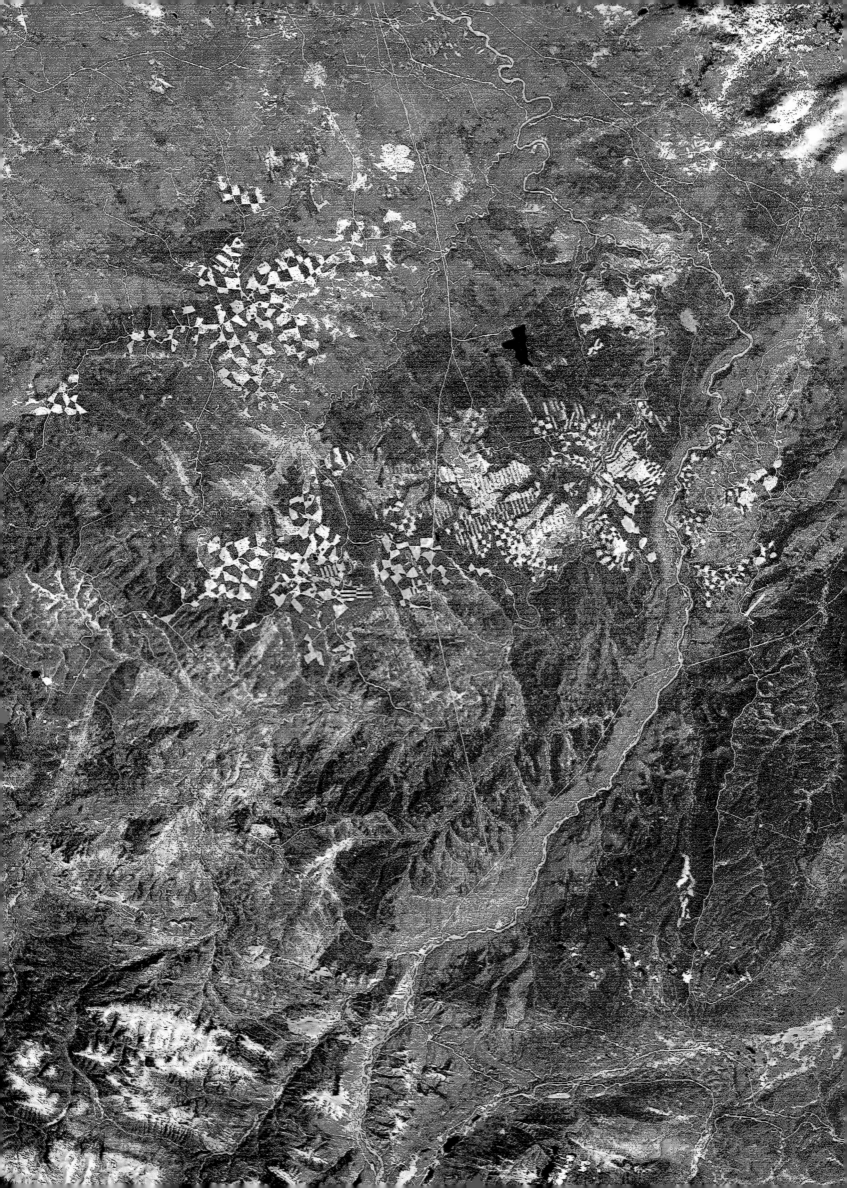

Shanghai and the Yangtze

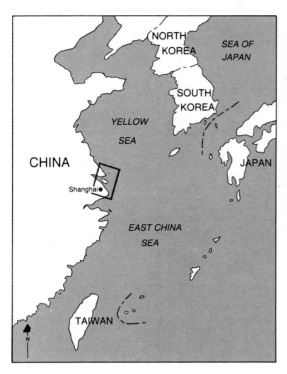

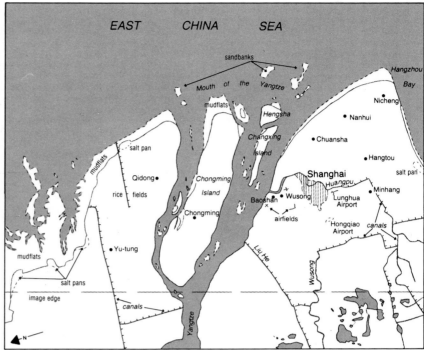

The Yangtze is China's longest river, running more than 6,300 kilometres (3,900 miles) to the East China Sea from its sources in the highlands of Tibet. Subject to huge floods and carrying with its waters millions of tonnes of sediment, at its mouth the Yangtze has built the great alluvial delta visible on the image overleaf. The swirls of blue and beige offshore provide evidence that the delta is still growing, at a rate estimated at about 1.5 kilometres a century. The three main islands within the river mouth, Chongming, Changxing, and Hengsha, have all been created from deposition of sand and silt, and there are extensive mudflats building on the left-hand coast of Chongming.

Shanghai, which vies with Tokyo for the title of the world's most populous city, is visible as a brown smudge on the dark-blue Huangpu River, in the right-hand side of the scene. Since its establishment as one of China's five Treaty Ports in the early 1840s, Shanghai has always been a major centre for foreign trade. It remains China's principal port for both imports and exports, and the country's leading centre for textiles, food processing, and manufacturing, but it is an unimpressive sight on this image. Most signs of its 11,000,000 inhabitants are lost, hidden within the red of the continuous heavy vegetation that covers the whole delta. Only the general form of the city can be seen, with the white lines of recent construction and airports surrounding it (Shanghai's main international airport, Hongqiao, lies a few miles below the city).

As this picture demonstrates, Shanghai sits within one of the world's most heavily cultivated regions.

With fertile soils, an equable climate, and the abundant supplies of water provided by the Yangtze, intensive farming and very high crop yields are possible. At the bottom of the scene, multiple-crop paddy rice is grown, with some dry-season vegetables. Vegetables are cultivated more heavily in a narrow zone around Shanghai, for mainly local use, and there are numerous hog farms in the same area.

A great network of irrigation canals, of which the principal ones are visible as dark blue and the smaller ones as fine white lines on the image, supplies water to the fields. It is estimated that there are 800,000 kilometres (500,000 miles) of canals and ditches within the delta. Closer to the coast, cotton is grown in two-crop rotation with rice, and along the outer periphery of the delta the fields are planted with cotton, orchards, and mulberry trees. It is a measure of the area's density of cultivation that there is little sign of the changing land use from rice in the bottom half to cotton at the top. Only slight colour differences indicate the changes; for example, the slightly browner reds on the left side of Chongming Island show areas where cotton and mulberries predominate, with rice grown on the right.

The whole delta is very fertile, except for saline strips along the coast. The far left of the image shows the clean lines of a man-made coastline, marking the boundary of the agriculture, and along these lines large salt pans appear as prominent black linear patterns with the brown fingers of saline mudflats stretching out many miles offshore. Salt pans are also visible on the right-hand edge of the image.

Image scale and date: 1 cm = 3.9 km, May 1978.

Development of Eastern Hokkaido, Japan

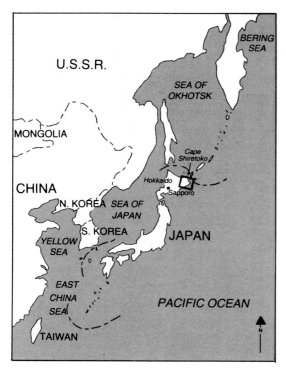

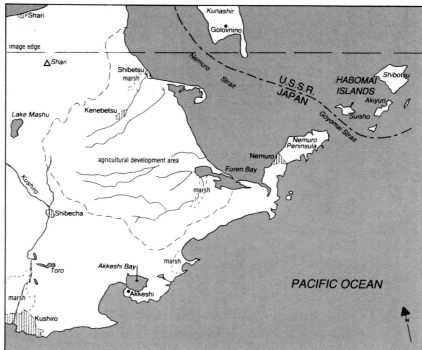

Japan is mainly a mountain land, covered by ranges that run through the country lengthwise from north to south. Three-quarters of the land area lies on steep hills, and most agricultural development is through intensive farming of small plots, just a few hectares in size. Every available level area that has not been taken over by urban development is used for crops. It is therefore a surprise to see, on the Japanese image on pages 124-5, a large, even plain covered by a regular grid of service roads, with few signs of towns and cities.

The mystery is solved as soon as we look at the location. This is eastern Hokkaido, the most northerly of the large islands that make up the country of Japan, and a region that until the second half of the last century was regarded as a remote frontier area. Even today, Hokkaido's 78,000 square kilometres (30,000 square miles) contain more than one-fifth of the country's land area, but less than 5 per cent of the people. More than 1 million of these live in Sapporo, the island's principal city, 240 kilometres (150 miles) west of the image area and the site of the 1972 Winter Olympics.

Hokkaido is remote not only geographically, but also culturally. Its native population was the 'hairy Ainu', a race of Caucasian origin, quite different from the rest of the Japanese people and well known to anthropologists as the most hirsute people on earth. Japanese from Honshu and the southern islands still tend to regard Hokkaido as pioneer country, too barbaric and cold for settlement.

As a consequence, Hokkaido has much more available open space than the rest of Japan. The area shown in this image is a plain at the eastern end of the island, running from the black bean-shape of Lake Mashu in the north to the blue patch of the city of Kushiro in the south. At the eastern extremity lies the snake-head of the Nemuro Peninsula, with the blue city of Nemuro visible half-way along it. Beyond the Nemuro Peninsula, and continuing its line across the Goyomai Strait, lie the Soviet-occupied Habomai Islands of Suisho, Akiyuri, and Shibotsu. The ownership of these islands has been in dispute since 1945. On the north-western edge is the beginning of a wooded range of mountains, coniferous forest stretching north to Cape Shiretoko (beyond the image area).

Hokkaido has short summers and cold winters with up to 2 metres of snow, so the agriculture of the area is restricted to a single crop per year. Rice remains the principal crop, though the climate and short growing season (120-150 frost-free days) encourage wheat, barley, potatoes, soya beans, and oats as increasingly popular alternatives. Dairy farming works well here, and much of the newly developed land on the scene is pasture. The general farming practices and land use in Hokkaido owe a great deal to two nineteenth-century Americans, William Clark Smith and Horace Capron, who founded the University of Hokkaido and were specialists in agricultural methods. Modern land layout still reflects their influence.

The curiously clear appearance of the road pattern in the newly-developing area of the image north of the swampy southern coast is the result of several different factors. The width of the roads and the areas that surround them are large, reflecting Hokkaido's low land cost; the population density is low, thus there is no urban development to mask linear road patterns; and the general wet and swampy nature of the terrain encourages the growth of weeds and grasses along the disturbed margins, to make the linear pattern more visible.

Image scale and date: 1 cm = 3.2 km, October 1980.

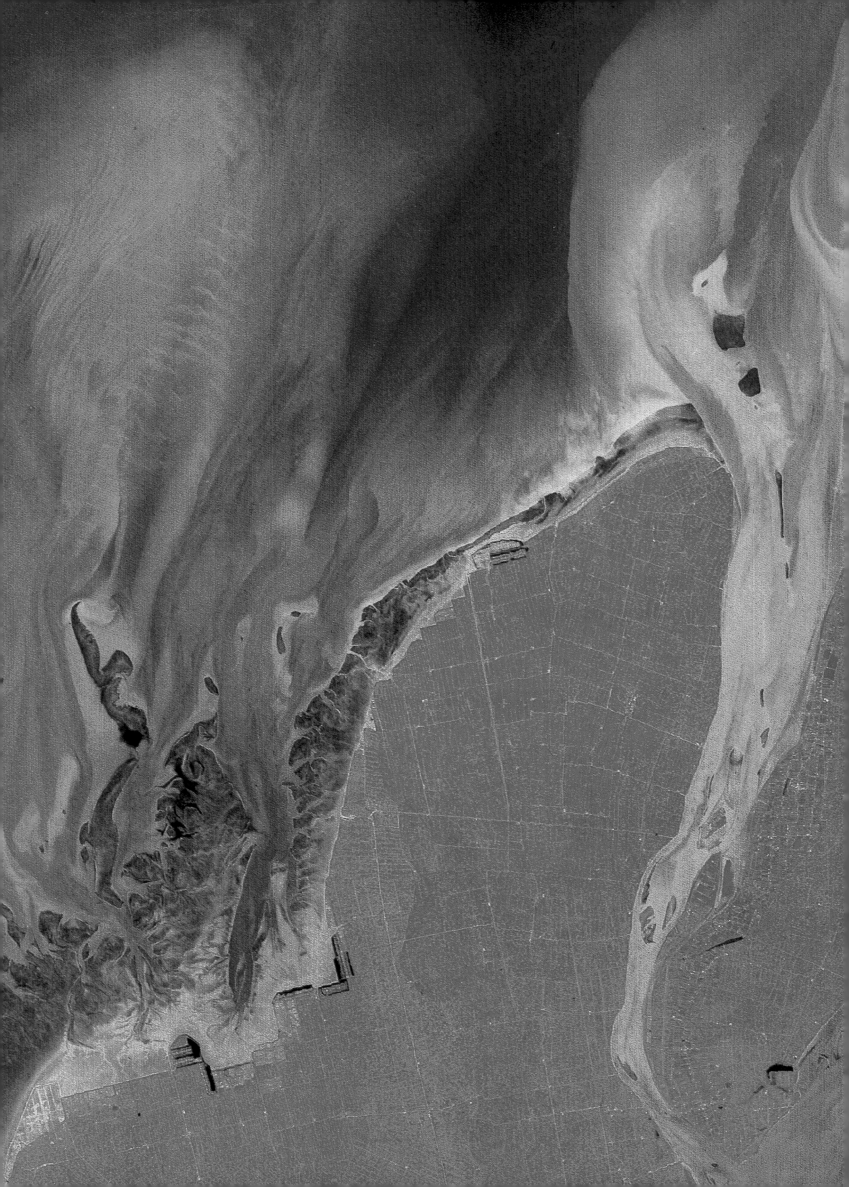

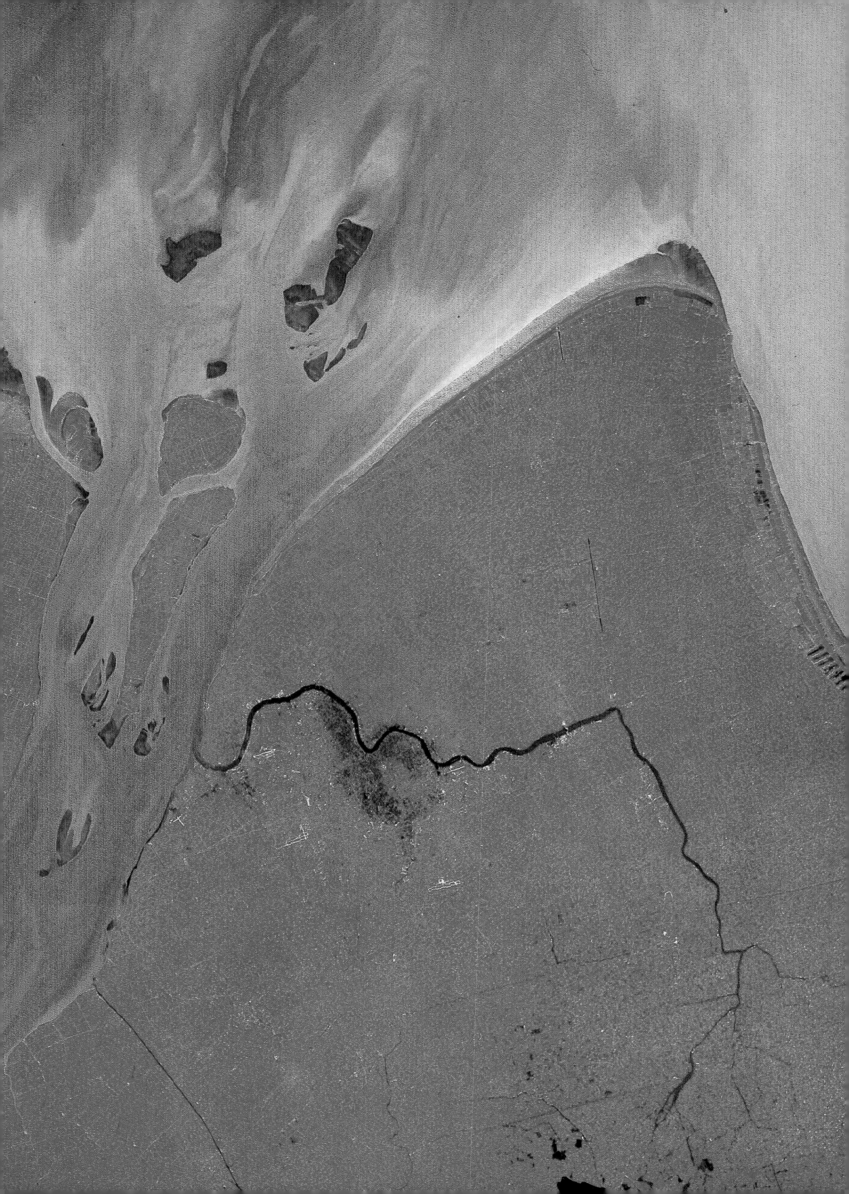

Perth and South-west Australia

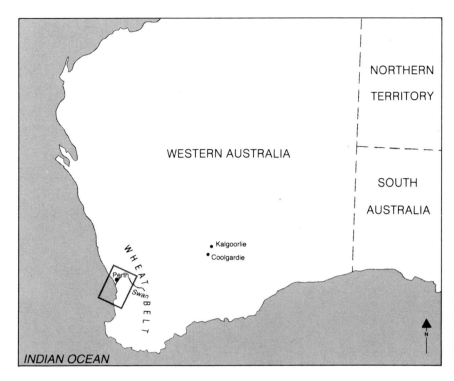

The state of Western Australia, with an area of 2,528,000 square kilometres (976,000 square miles), is exceeded in size by only seven countries of the world. However, its population is little more than 1 million people. In so under-populated a region, it is no surprise that the development of the area's full agricultural potential has hardly begun.

This image shows the western and most heavily populated portion of the state, with the capital and biggest city, Perth (metropolitan-area population 800,000), visible near the coast in the lower half of the scene. Perth lies north of a broadening of the Swan River known as Melville Water, and shows as a patch of blue above the black water. Not much detail is visible within the city, but the crossed runways of Perth Airport are visible below the river to the east, while the dark-red patch of Kings Park shows clearly to the west, on the north shore of Melville Water. Further south and west, Fremantle, the principal port for Western Australia, can be seen where the river meets the Indian Ocean. Perth and Fremantle provide the export points for Western Australia's wheat, cattle, wool, gold, timber, oil, and minerals.

The general structure of the area is clear from the image. There is a coastal plain, broad at the top of the picture but narrowing as it reaches Perth and continues on to Rockingham and Safety Bay at the southern end of the scene. Sand dunes broken by limestone reefs show as small, bright whitish patches along the coast, which is clearly defined by the white line of sandy beaches. Garden and Rottnest Islands, eroded reef remnants, are visible offshore.

South of Perth and the Canning River there is a long winter rainy season (80-140 centimetres; 30-55 inches a year), enough to support a thriving cattle, vegetable, and citrus fruit business; but to the north the poor calcareous soils, deficient in copper, limit food production to some beef cattle and a few sheep.

The coastal plain is bordered inland by the clean dark-red line of the wooded Darling Range. The edge of the range is a fertile clay, but this quickly gives way to the ancient granites and gneisses of the range's main plateau, 500 metres (1,600 feet) above sea-level. The jarrah tree provides the main cover for the Darling Range, together with eucalyptus, pines, and karri gums. Extensive bauxite mines on the western edge of the range show as green and white patches amongst the red vegetation. Patches of light pink there indicate that some reforestation has already taken place.

Beyond the Darling Range, in the north-east corner of the image, there is another clear change of land cover. Now we are in a drier white-and-grey inland region, where rainfall is only 40-50 centimetres (15-20 inches) a year, all in the winter months. This is the beginning of Western Australia's great wheat-growing belt, which sweeps south to the coast, 320 kilometres (200 miles) beyond the image edge. In this autumn March scene (we are 32 degrees south of the equator) the winter wheat and barley are being planted, and not yet showing the red of sprouted growth. The large area to be cultivated, the moderate crop yields, and the very low population dictate the use of mechanized farm equipment and big fields.

North-east of the eastern wheat belt, off the image area, lie the great Coolgardie and Kalgoorlie goldfields, whose discovery, in 1892 and 1893, started the West Australian Gold Rush, and stimulated the development of Perth, Fremantle, and the south-west corner of this continent.

Image scale and date: 1 cm = 4.8 km, March 1979.

Capital Cities

Although data from the Landsat series of spacecraft have now been used in scores of applications from the prediction of infectious disease to monitoring of illegal waste dumping, the original system design concentrated on use in agriculture and geology. Images that cover thousands of square kilometres, but offer little detail smaller than a field, were the result. Given that emphasis, it is not surprising that the limitations of Landsat images are most clearly revealed in scenes of urban areas.

A picture element, or pixel, is the smallest individual area that is sampled by the spacecraft's sensor system. It represents a rectangle on the ground roughly 79 metres by 57 metres (260 feet by 190 feet). If ground features smaller than this are visible, it is only because they are in strong contrast to their surroundings and modify the appearance of the whole surrounding picture element enough to provide a visible change. In the extreme case, reflected sunlight from a half-metre (2-foot) mirror will show on a Landsat image as a brighter pixel, though the placement of the mirror within the 60-metre (200-foot) pixel cannot be determined.

In the same way, bridges across deep water can often be seen, even though they may be no more than 20 metres across, while roads and freeways of the same size are lost against the background of urban development of similar materials. Similarly, individual buildings, gardens, streets, and memorials are rarely visible within a city. What can be seen, and very clearly, is the year-to-year change and growth of built-up area, since the asphalt and concrete of a town appears quite different on Landsat images from woods and fields.

The capital cities shown in this chapter exemplify these points. They range from the very old (Vienna and Paris) to the new and rapidly developing (Buenos Aires). As a general rule, the newer outlying suburbs of all these cities reveal more interior detail than the old centres. The latter have narrower streets, smaller buildings, a weathered appearance, and were usually built of locally available surface materials. As a result they appear less bright on the images, and blend more into their general surroundings.

Since the visible features of the earth often fail to fall neatly into separate categories, many national capitals appear elsewhere in this book in other contexts. Athens, Rome, Istanbul and Cairo will be found in 'The Ancient World'; Jerusalem and Amsterdam in 'Shaping the Earth'; Cape Town (the seat of South Africa's Parliament) in 'Commerce and Trade'; Nicosia in 'The Search for Energy and Minerals'; Moscow and Tai-pei in 'Strategic Pressure Points'.

To readers who say, 'But where is London? Peking? Tehran? Washington? Santiago? Manila? Tokyo? Montevideo?' we again refer them to the earlier and companion volume, *Earthwatch*.

Buenos Aires

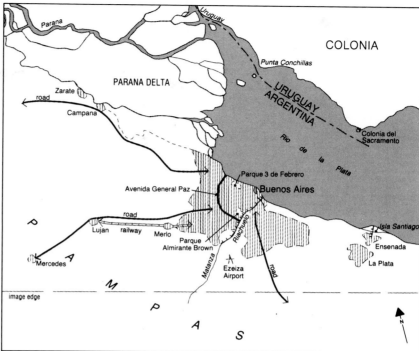

Three hundred years ago Buenos Aires was a collection of mud huts with a population of no more than 1,000. Today, Buenos Aires is South America's biggest city, with a metropolitan population of over 9 million — more than one-third of the total number of Argentina's inhabitants. The city shows overleaf as a great sprawling area of blue and grey on the south shore of the Rio de la Plata. Buenos Aires is the country's centre for transportation although, as the sedimented swirls of the river suggest, it is difficult for large vessels to reach the city. Ships of up to 8.5 metres (28 feet) draft can reach here, but only by following a winding, difficult channel in the shallow estuary. The country's railways, whose dark lines run parallel to the major roads and are hardly visible, were constructed with British capital and staff in the last century. They were built to connect all parts of the country with Buenos Aires, and today all Argentina's roads, rail, and shipping centre on the city.

Within the city, a number of its most prominent features can be seen on the image. The boundary of its federal district is marked to the west and south by the fine black semi-circular line of the 24-kilometre (15-mile) Avenida General Paz, and to the east by the Riachuelo canal which the avenue meets near the red patches of the Parque Almirante Brown on the left of the waterway. Further south the Riachuelo becomes the Matanza River, and to the right of it the pale-blue lines, looking like an 'A', of the city's Ezeiza Airport can be seen. On the shore just to the left of the dark older section of the city lies the Parque 3 de Febrero, visible as a white and red spot. The blue-white threads of major roads can be traced outwards from Buenos Aires to Lujan and Mercedes to the west, and to Campana and Zarate in the north-west. La Plata, 53 kilometres (33 miles) east of Buenos Aires, is a

substantial city with more than half a million people and thriving industries. It is Argentina's second port, although with only about 10 per cent of the foreign traffic of Buenos Aires, and it is the refining centre for Argentinian oil. Ensenada, the port for La Plata, is situated nearly 5 kilometres (3 miles) inland and connects with the sea through a canal, clearly visible on this image where it crosses the bright red of the Isla Santiago.

To the north across the Rio de la Plata lies the Colonia Province of Uruguay, and the different land use there contributes to the remarkable diversity of colours seen in this early summer picture. Near the Uruguay River in the centre of the image the main cultivation is single-crop wheat, seen as fields of grey and drab green. Further east this is mixed with maize and flax, while near the right-hand edge of the scene, east of Colonia del Sacramento, the brighter red of the fields marks a change of land use to pasture and cattle-raising.

The north-west corner of the scene is occupied by the vivid crimson and black of the Parana Delta, through which various branches of the Parana River pass on their way to the estuary of the Rio de la Plata. This is swampy, non-agricultural land, supporting only grasses and wetland vegetation. To the west and south lies the broad, fertile plain of the Pampas, which west of Lujan grows mainly wheat and sunflowers, while south of Buenos Aires near the bottom of the image the land is devoted to dairy production and the raising of beef cattle (Argentina is one of the world's leading exporters of beef). Along the shore from Buenos Aires to La Plata and beyond is a brighter strip of red where the generally marshy land is used for fruit and vegetable production.

Image scale and date: 1 cm = 3.9 km, December 1981.

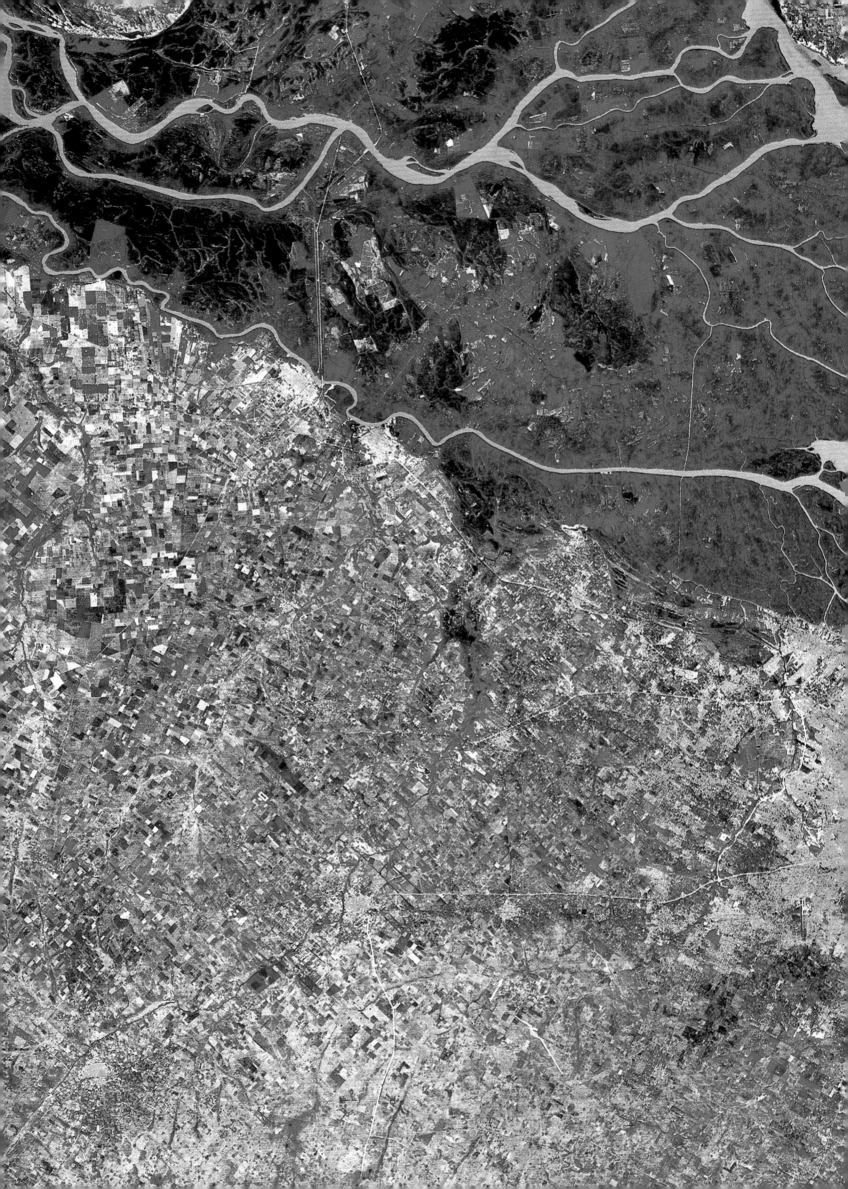

Oslo

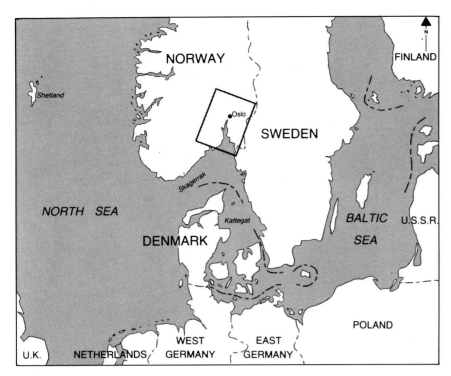

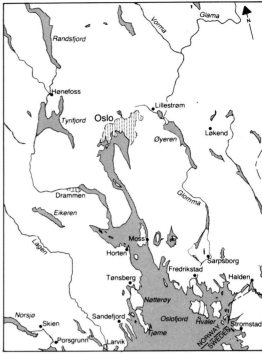

Norway is a long, narrow country, stretching from Lindesnes, at 58 degrees (the latitude of northern Scotland), to Nordkinn, which at 71 degrees is the most northern point of mainland Europe. Although the country is more than 1,800 kilometres (1,100 miles) long, it is narrow along most of that length, averaging only 100 kilometres (60 miles) wide; at Ofotfjord, in the far north, it narrows to 8 kilometres (5 miles).

This image shows part of southern Norway, with the capital and principal port, Oslo, visible as a blue patch at the head of the long north-pointing Oslofjord. At a latitude of almost 60 degrees, Oslo is the most northerly of the world's capitals except for Helsinki and Reykjavik. In spite of this, its climate is surprisingly mild, and the port of Oslo is ice-free and accessible all the year round. Norway, particularly on the west and south coasts, is warmed by the Gulf Stream, and this provides the unusually high temperatures enjoyed by the shore areas.

However, as this image makes clear, south Norway is not a productive agricultural area. This is a consequence of geology and the actions of ancient glaciers rather than climate. We see on this picture high, eroded plateaux of ancient granites and gneisses, the oldest rocks in Europe, split by the narrow water-filled valleys of the fjords. The fjords, scoured by glaciers, are present through most of the country, and they are usually steep-sided as well as deep. Tyrifjord, in the upper left quadrant of the image, has a depth of 270 metres (900 feet). The uplands, also swept by

long-ago ice flows, have little topsoil. Only the limited land on the coast or in rare inland plains, filled with glacial debris, is usable for agriculture.

Oslofjord, occupying the lower part of the image, is not characteristic of Norwegian topography. It is quite broad and shallow, and it is surrounded by Norway's most extensive lowlands. Cleared agricultural areas can be seen as whiter patches and strips throughout the picture, where the principal crops of rye, barley, and oats are grown, together with some wheat. Only about 1 per cent of the country is used to cultivate crops, with another 2 per cent grassland. The valleys are also the centres of population, and a number of blue urban patches, in addition to Oslo itself, can be seen, notably Drammen, Moss, Fredrikstad, and Sarpsborg. The grassy valley slopes are used for pasture, but the brownish-red areas over the rest of the image indicate coniferous forest, uncultivated and almost unpopulated. Of the country's 4 million people, about 650,000 of them live in Oslo, and this image area is the most heavily populated of the whole country.

In the south part of Oslofjord where it opens into the Skagerrak (just off the image to the south) are numerous islands, which continue round the whole western shore of the country, and up into the Arctic. They form a characteristic coastal fringe of the country, known locally as the *Skjaergaard*, or wall of sheltering islands. The lower right-hand corner of the image is actually a part of Sweden.

Image scale and date: 1 cm = 5.5 km, September 1981.

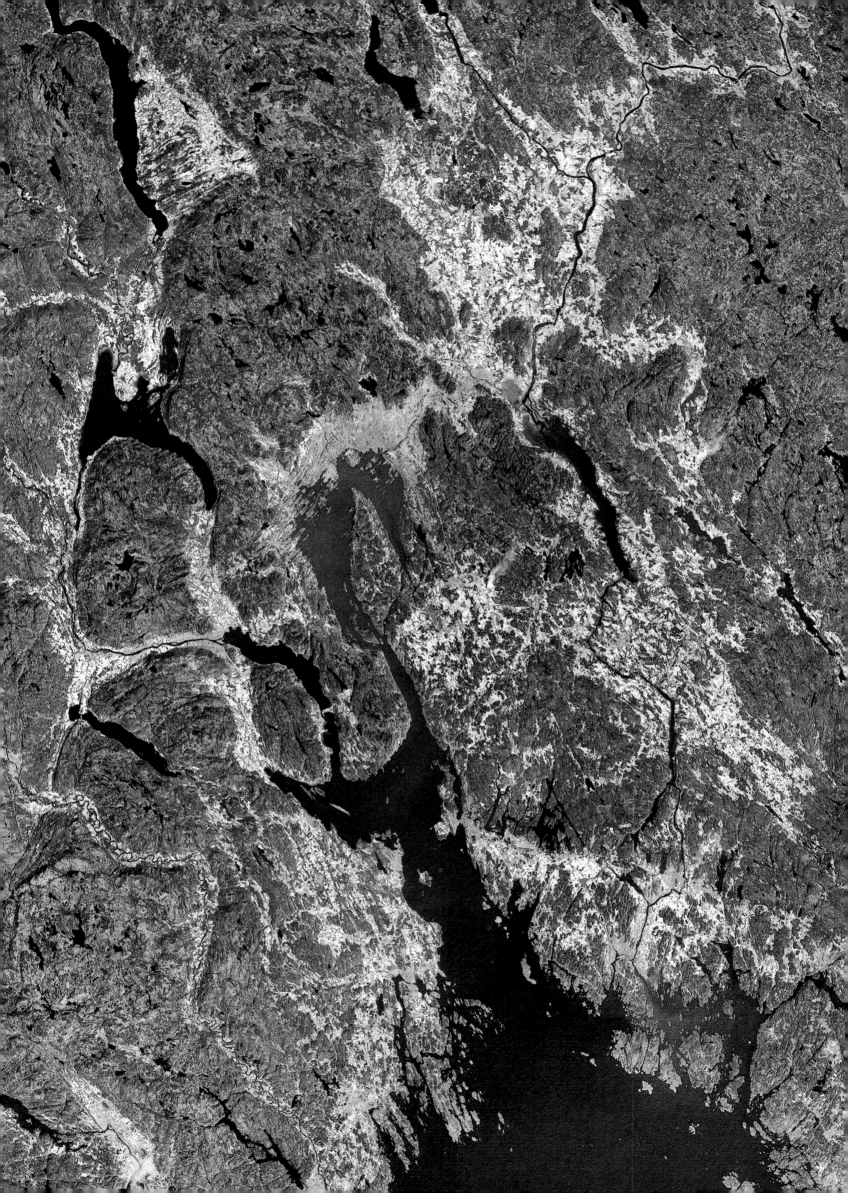

Jakarta

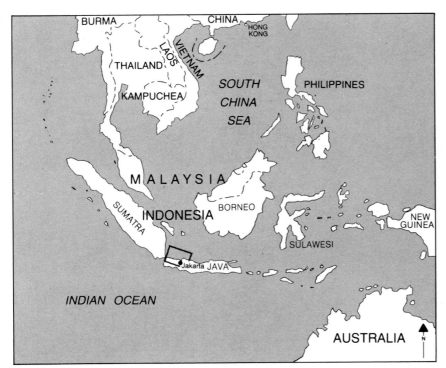

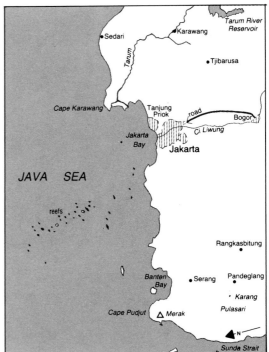

Indonesia's population is now up to 140,000,000. The total area of the scattered system of islands is large, with over 1,900,000 square kilometres (nearly 750,000 square miles) of land, but the people are not evenly distributed. More than half of the population live on Java, the 130,000-square-kilometre (50,000-square-mile) island whose north-west corner is seen in this image. Jakarta, the country's capital, is visible on the shore slightly above centre. It is the government and commercial centre for Indonesia, and the home for 6.5 million people in one of the world's most densely populated areas.

The evidence of growing population pressure can be seen in this picture. Two hundred years ago, Java was famous for its great teak forests, with their apparently unlimited supplies of hardwood. Today, the forests are visible as areas of red only on the higher ground above and below Bogor, inland towards the middle of the island. The coastal plains have been cleared and are now *sawah,* irrigated farmland whose crops, mainly rice, support the people. Java is close to the equator, there is no cold season, and the soil is enriched by ash from the country's numerous active volcanoes; thus two or even three crops a year are possible. Corn, cassava, coconut, sago, peanuts, soya beans and fruit are grown in addition to rice, all for domestic consumption. Principal export crops from Jakarta are rubber, tea, and quinine.

Modern Jakarta is a sprawling, unstructured city, extending far inland. Its port facilities are clearly visible at Tandjung Priok, with modern docks and wharves jutting into Jakarta Bay and lying parallel to the shore. Old Jakarta, the centre portion of today's city, was built by the Dutch along the Ci Liwung River. The river cannot be seen on the image but its fine system of canals is visible as a pattern of dark lines within the city. To the right of Jakarta the road to Bogor shows as a fine blue line through red and green fields. Both cities changed their names in 1945, at the time of Indonesia's declaration of independence. Jakarta was formerly Batavia, a Dutch name it had held since 1619. Bogor used to be Buitenzorg, and was the home of the governors of Java after 1745. Although the climate of west Java is normally equable, it can be rough in places — Bogor has thunderstorms 300 days of the year on average. The bright blue water body at the top of the image is the Tarum River Reservoir.

In the lower part of the picture, above Cape Pudjut, Banten Bay is visible. Banten (formerly known as Bantam) was Java's historic trading site with Europe. It was active in Elizabethan times, and the chosen port for East India Company operations. Below it in the Sunda Strait lies the island of Krakatoa, 30 kilometres (20 miles) off the image edge. The volcanic explosion there in 1883 was the greatest recorded in modern times. It sent tidal waves across all the shorelines seen on this picture, and killed 36,000 Indonesians.

Offshore, the Java Sea is shallow and full of reefs. A number of these, at or even slightly below the surface, can be seen below Jakarta Bay. Knowledge of the location of reefs often depends on surveys that date back to the early part of the last century. Today, updated maps are being produced directly from satellite images similar to this one.

Image scale and date: 1 cm = 5.8 km, June 1976.

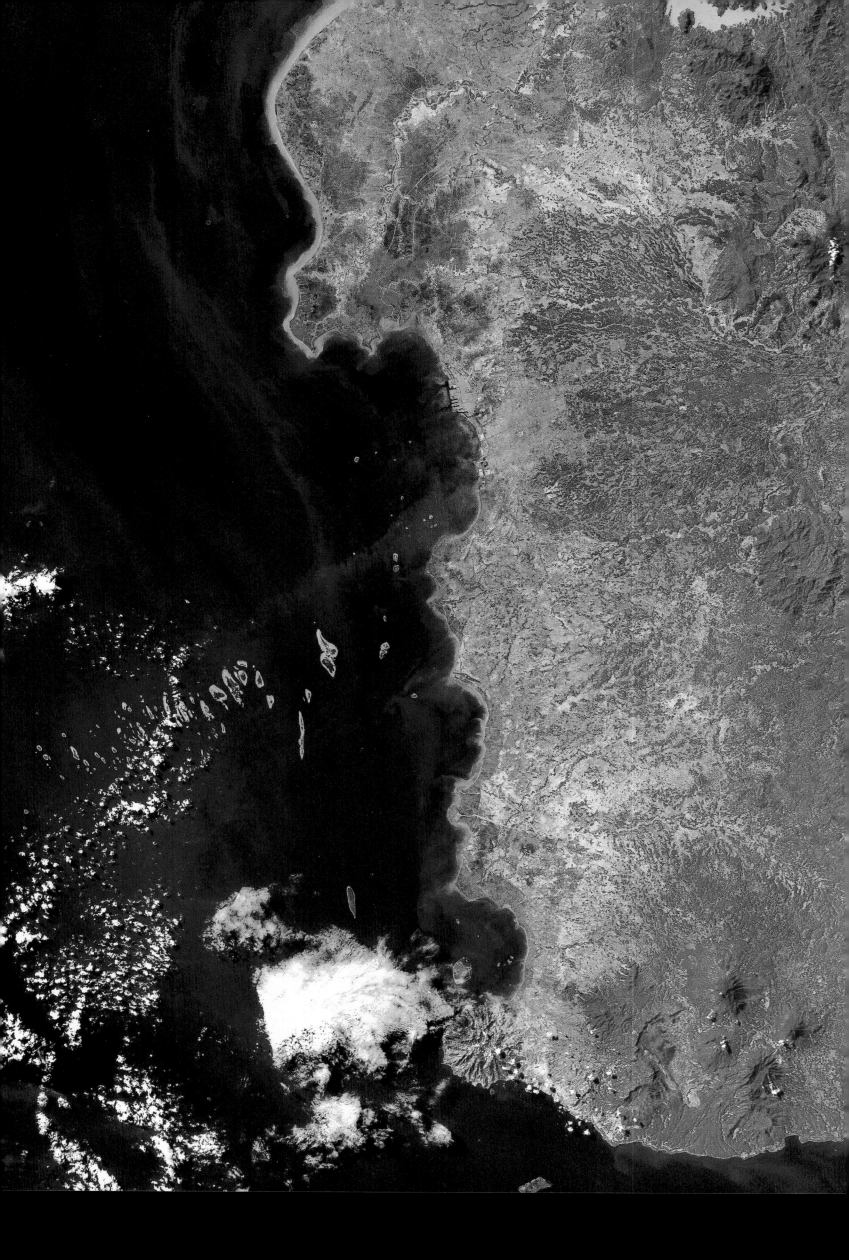

Paris

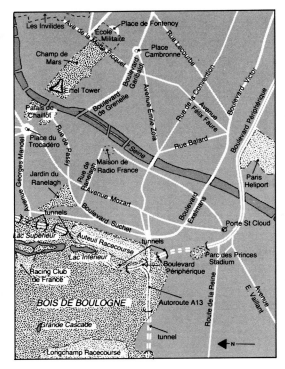

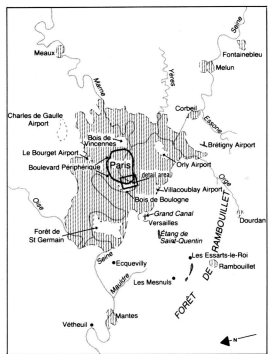

Paris is the leading industrial and commercial city of France, with a population of nearly 10 million. This springtime image shows many of the city's best-known features.

The River Seine is everywhere visible as it snakes its way through the centre of Paris, from its meeting with the Marne, near the centre of the scene, all the way down to the bottom edge. The Bois de Boulogne, Forêt de St Germain, Bois de Vincennes and other Paris woods and parks show as red patches within the blue-grey of the city. Beyond the city, forested areas appear as a darker red against the pattern of fields. The blue area that looks like a lake in the left side of the Forêt de St Germain is in fact a railway station. The two major airports stand out clearly: Charles de Gaulle to the left of the top of the city, a blue and white patch amid the red fields, and Orly to the right, a fine pattern of white lines on a red vegetated background.

To the right of the Seine, not far from the Forêt de St Germain, stands Versailles. The famous gardens show as a red vegetated area, roughly triangular, with the Grand Canal just visible as a dark-blue cross.

This feature, 1.5 kilometres (1 mile) long but only 60 metres (200 feet) wide, is at the limit of what can be seen with the first generation of earth-observing satellites. A foretaste of what will be available in the near future is shown in the additional detail image on this page. It is a simulation, produced by computer-processing an image from an airborne scanner, of the pictures that will be obtained when the French S.P.O.T. (Système Probatoire d'Observation de la Terre) satellite is launched in 1984. Details down to 10 metres (33 feet) across will be visible, and stereoscopic coverage will also be available. The example shown here is at a scale about eight times that of the main image. As any street map of Paris will verify, S.P.O.T. permits the identification and accurate mapping of all major thoroughfares, parks, large buildings, and bridges. Notice the shadow of the Eiffel Tower in the upper left of the detail, at the northern end of the Champ de Mars.

Image scale and date: 1 cm = 3.9 km, April 1976.
Detail scale and date: 1 cm = 0.5 km, September 1981.

Khartoum

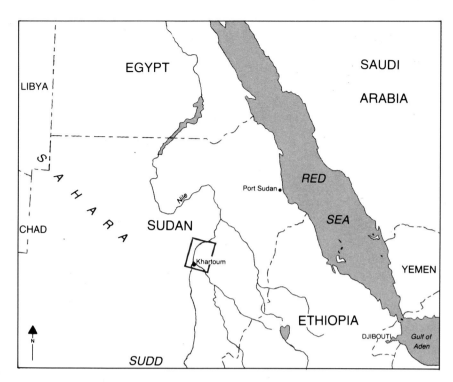

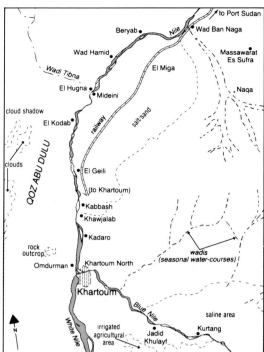

Sudan stretches south from the dry Sahara Desert to the humid swamp of the Sudd, a vast marsh the size of Scotland, and to the equatorial grasslands beyond it. Independent since 1956 after a half century of joint British-Egyptian government, Sudan is of great size but small resources. Close to its centre lies Khartoum, the nation's capital and the cultural meeting place of the Arabs of northern Sudan and the tribal Africans of the grasslands in the south. The city lies on one of the main pilgrim routes from Africa to Mecca. This image shows the confluence at Khartoum of the White Nile on the west and the Blue Nile on the east, with the merged rivers continuing their way north to Egypt and the Mediterranean.

Khartoum is visible as a dark patch lying between the White Nile and the Blue Nile, just where the rivers meet. Khartoum, 'Elephant's Trunk' in Arabic, was so named because of the way that the Blue Nile curves above the city. Immediately to the west lies the town of Omdurman, and to the north across the Blue Nile is Khartoum North. The three today form a single development, with a combined population of almost 1.5 million. This is the only urban area of significance in the whole of Sudan, and it has doubled in size in the past ten years.

The region is a dry semi-desert, with a rainfall of 13-25 centimetres (5-10 inches) a year, all in the summer months. Now, in early October, the usually dry wadis show bright red with vegetation, but there is not enough water to permit agriculture without irrigation from the Nile. Every perennial river here is part of the Nile system. The wadis run through a yellow undulating plain of sand dunes and gravelly clays, the *qoz,* which are porous enough to absorb all rainfall but fertile enough to support gum-bearing

acacias that provide camel fodder and a valuable export. Gum arabic, collected from acacias in the Qoz Abu Dulu to the north-west, is shipped from Khartoum to the Red Sea via a railroad, built in 1906 and visible on the image as a shadowy dark line through the infertile grey-white salt and sand flats east of the curving river. Rocky outcrops of basalt and granite produce black patches on the image, often with sharply defined boundaries that in the north-east of the picture etch delicate patterns like dried leaves on the yellow background of the dunes and aridosol soils.

Khartoum was founded following an Egyptian invasion in 1820, but it reached its peak of fame later in the century when the Mahdi and his army of dervishes besieged General Gordon and a British force there in 1884. A relief group arrived along the Nile on 25 January 1885, three days too late. Gordon was dead and Khartoum had fallen. Kitchener and the Nile Expeditionary Force later completely defeated the dervishes at Omdurman in 1898, in one of history's most one-sided battles (11,000 dervishes were killed, and forty-eight members of the Nile Expeditionary Force). In the intervening years since Gordon's death Khartoum had been abandoned. When Kitchener rebuilt the city, he chose a street plan with the layout of the Union Jack. However, it would take a strong imagination to see that pattern on this image. Modern Khartoum shows only as a regular grid of darker streets on the grey background of clay soil.

The dark red patterning at the bottom edge of the image is the northern limit of the irrigation scheme described and displayed on pages 113-15. The red patches higher up, nearer the confluence of the White and Blue Nile, are also agricultural developments.

Image scale and date: 1 cm = 5.3 km, October 1972.

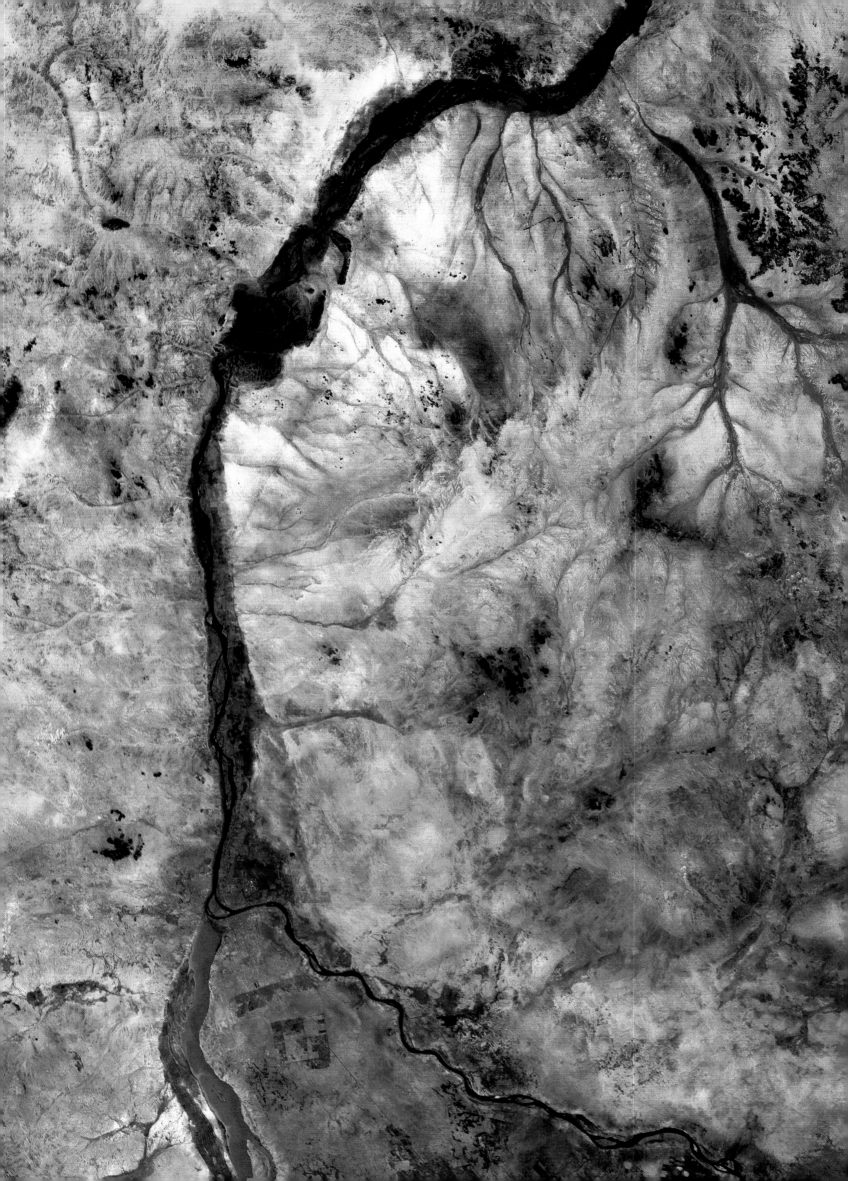

Vienna

Traditionally regarded as the crossroads of Europe, Austria shares borders with many countries: Czechoslovakia in the north-east; Hungary in the south-east; Yugoslavia and Italy in the south; Switzerland and Liechtenstein in the west; and West Germany in the north. Vienna, the Austrian capital, lies near the eastern and northern borders of the country, and is visible as a patch of darker blue in the lower right quadrant of this spring image.

The Danube, the greatest river of central Europe, flows west to east across the southern part of the image and can be seen as a blue ribbon at the centre of a bright red strip of river meadows and woods. The Danube passes through Vienna, and within the city the natural river flow has been channelled for flood control. Its old course now shows as a loop of dark lake, on the blue canal's north bank. The city, once a fort of the Roman Empire, and in the eighteenth and nineteenth centuries a centre of European arts and culture, is now the home of 1.5 million people (one-fifth of Austria's total population).

Surrounding Vienna the principal topographic areas of eastern Austria can be distinguished on the image from the patterns of agriculture and land use. To the south the long northern extension of forest that runs from the bottom of the picture up to the western edge of the city is the Vienna Woods, a famous scenic area, and a terminus for the Alps. Vienna is at the south-west end of a fertile region known as the Vienna Basin, seen here as the intensely cultivated pattern of fields that covers the centre of the image.

This is the country's most productive farming area, and the main crops are wheat, barley, sugar beets and corn, with vineyards common in the southern part. At the northern edge of the Basin, root crops and cereals predominate. Areas of poorer soil, steeper slope, and poor drainage remain uncultivated, and show as bright red forested patches.

The Czechoslovakian border runs across the upper right quadrant of the picture. An approximate border line can be traced on the image simply from the pronounced difference in agricultural practices in the two countries. Fields in Czechoslovakia are much bigger, there are more cleared areas of light-blue, and there is nowhere the same intensity of cultivation. In the upper left of the image the agriculture becomes noticeably less as we approach the higher ground of the Bohemian Plateau. This is a poorly drained area, much of it left as forest and the remainder only moderately productive.

The whole left side of the image, from Vienna west to the Bohemian Plateau, is famous for its scenic attractions. However, the general rural nature of the Austrian countryside around Vienna has been changing, largely as a result of geological discoveries in the area. Substantial oil and gas reserves exist at Zistersdorf, in the centre right of the picture near the Czechoslovakian border. At Linz, 75 kilometres (45 miles) beyond the left-hand image boundary, the discovery of iron deposits has formed the basis for a thriving iron and steel industry.

Image scale and date: 1 cm = 5 km, May 1979.

140

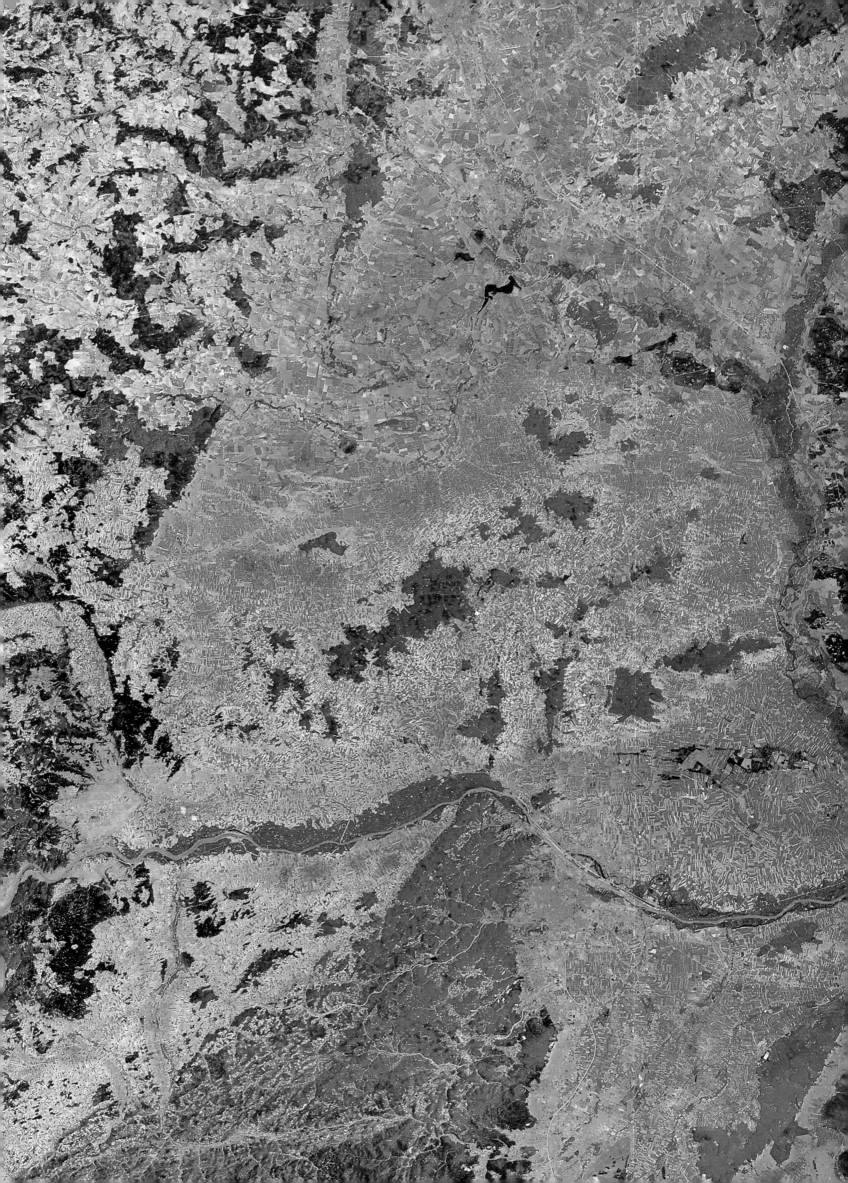

Rangoon

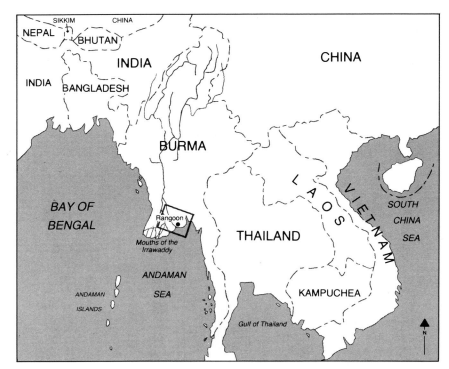

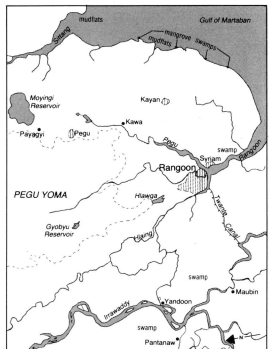

Burma is a country of contradictions: it has great mineral resources of silver, lead, zinc, tin, oil and tungsten, but is still dominated by an agricultural economy. Of its population of 35 million, more than three-quarters are involved in some aspect of farming. This image shows the south central part of the country, with the capital, Rangoon, visible as a dark, amorphous patch just to the right of the centre of the scene. Rangoon is a city of over 2 million people, standing 40 kilometres (25 miles) from the sea on the promontory formed at the confluence of the Hlaing and Pegu rivers. It is the country's centre for commerce and transportation, and also the principal manufacturing city of Burma.

Part of the great river of Burma, the Irrawaddy, can be seen at the bottom of the image, a meandering blue band full of divisions and re-connections. This forms one of the nine major deltaic branches of the Irrawaddy. Another branch is the much narrower and fainter Hlaing River, running below Rangoon to the Gulf of Martaban. Although the Hlaing River carries only a small fraction of the waters of the Irrawaddy, it provides navigable access upstream for 1,500 kilometres (900 miles). As its light-blue tone suggests, the Irrawaddy is a turbid, muddy river, carrying heavy sediments to the gulf and building a great delta on the south coast of Burma. In the flood season the carried sediments colour the water many kilometres out in the Andaman Sea.

The Sittang River can be seen at the upper edge of the picture, with dark clumps and swirls of mudflats prominent in its blue estuary. Originally an independent river, the Sittang now shares its headwaters with the Irrawaddy, far to the north. Prominent bright red patches of mangrove swamp are visible on the mudflats and along the shore of the Gulf of Martaban.

This picture was taken during the cool, dry season, which runs from October to February. Later in the year, during the monsoon months of May to September, the whole south part of the scene that now appears as a speckled pattern of blue and grey will show the bright red of paddy rice. Here it shows only the numerous orange-red spots of individual towns and villages, each growing its dry-season crop of vegetables. Originally forested, this region was cleared in the nineteenth century and has become the country's principal rice-growing province.

The bright orange mass filling the left centre of this image is the Pegu Yoma, forested hills, mostly of evergreens, that rise 750 metres (2,500 feet) above the alluvial lowlands. The pink tones of rain forest and grasslands can be seen as island areas growing within the dark patch of the Moyingi Reservoir, just above the Pegu Yoma. In the lower part of the image, within the Irrawaddy delta, a mixture of dark patches of water and brighter orange-red tones indicates a low-lying swampy area. Here the land cover is grasses and shrubs, merging into true swamp at the bottom right of the picture.

Image scale and date: 1 cm = 5.7 km, January 1974.

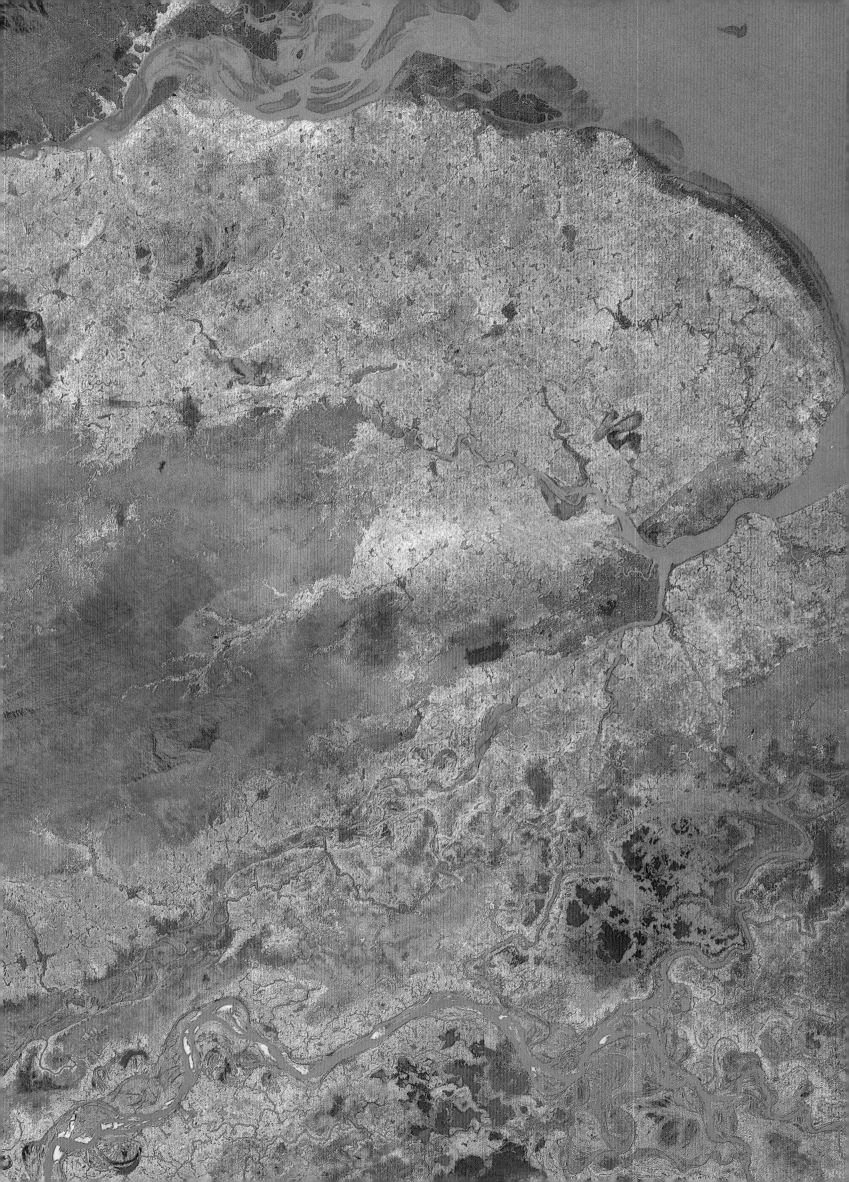

Stockholm

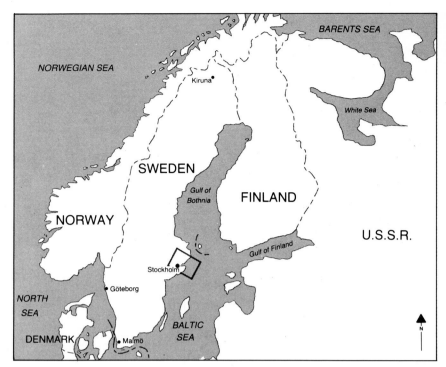

This part of Sweden is in the eastern lowlands, far different in climate and topography from the western mountain ranges that form the Scandinavian 'backbone' and the natural boundary with Norway. Stockholm, the Swedish capital, is visible as a large blue patch in the right centre of the image. Mälaren dominates the area below the city, and is a prominent part of a long complex of connected lakes and fjords that run almost across the country, from Norway to the Baltic Sea. Nearly 10 per cent of Sweden's area is covered by lakes, and the biggest of them lie within and to the immediate west of the image area. The lakes were created in the Pleistocene era, when heavy glaciation scooped them from ancient Scandinavian rocks that constitute the oldest surface formations in Europe.

Above the city, Saltsjö can be seen, an island-strewn inlet linking Stockholm with the sea. Offshore in the Baltic Sea at the top of the picture are numerous other islands, a part of the *Skjaergaard,* the protective island chain that rings most of the Scandinavian peninsula and was referred to earlier on page 132, in the discussion of the Oslo scene. The chain is at its densest near Stockholm, in the area covered by this image.

Stockholm is Sweden's biggest city, with a metropolitan-area population of 1.3 million in a country of little more than 8 million people. It lies close to sea-level and spreads over both sides of the channel connecting Saltsjö and Mälaren, and over the islands within that channel. Stockholm is a major centre for iron and steel production, and for engineering and shipbuilding. It is also the country's

principal port for imports, though in export trade it is exceeded in volume by Malmö, on the southern tip of Sweden, and by Göteborg on the west coast (both off the image).

The lowland plains that surround Stockholm are mainly fertile clays and permit good agricultural development. In this scene the cleared farmlands show as pale blue-white, lighter than the blue patches of towns and cities, and easily distinguished from the grey-green and reddish-brown of forests. The principal crops grown in the four and a half frost-free months enjoyed here are oats, potatoes, sugar beets, and hay, the last as a winter food for the numerous dairy herds maintained in this region.

North-west of Stockholm, Sigtuna is just about visible at the left side of Mälaren. This was once one of Sweden's most important towns, the residence of the royal family and the location of the mint; but its influence declined as Stockholm's grew. Although Stockholm's Bromma Airport cannot be distinguished from its urban background on this image, the runways of Arlanda Airport above Sigtuna are visible. Beyond Sigtuna, further to the left and lower down the image, lies the light-blue patch of Uppsala, site of ancient Swedish monuments and home of the country's principal and oldest university (founded 1477).

In the bottom left-hand corner, beyond Uppsala, begin the coniferous forests of Scots pine, spruce and beech that cover most of the country up to its northern boundary. Near that boundary, at Kiruna 900 kilometres (550 miles) beyond the image area, stands the Landsat ground receiving station that recorded this scene.

Image scale and date: 1 cm = 4.2 km, June 1980.

The Changing Wilderness

Two centuries ago, more than three-quarters of the world's land area was in its natural condition, undeveloped, unmapped, and often unexplored. Africa was still the dark continent, North America was colonized only on the coastal margins, South America was mainly of interest as a cornucopia of gold and silver, Australia was a ragged coastline and a mysterious interior, and Antarctica was no more than a rumour. Even in the Old World, vast areas were still *terra incognita* to the western nations. Northern Siberia, the Gobi and Takla Makan deserts, Tibet, the Arabian Peninsula, and the East Indies were blanks on the map, some of them inaccessible, others inhospitable, and a few forbidden.

Today, almost the whole earth has been mapped and there are few unexplored wilderness areas. The extent of what remains on different continents can be roughly gauged by the population density – an informative technique, but necessarily a crude one since distribution within an area can be highly inhomogeneous. Asia, for example, ranges from less than one person in every 2 square kilometres in Tibet and western China, to 4,000 per square kilometre in Hong Kong. This continent, with about 30 per cent of the world's land area, supports 60 per cent of the human race. Europe is even more densely packed, with 17 per cent of the species on only 6 per cent of the world's land.

Everywhere else is comparatively empty, with large remaining wilderness areas. The New World accounts for only 14 per cent of the world population, on 28 per cent of the area. Australia, with a tiny 0.3 per cent of the people and 5 per cent of the land area, is looked on with longing by many of the over-populated nations; and Antarctica, which represents one-tenth of the world's land, remains as pure wilderness, unpopulated except for occasional research and exploration teams.

Many people regard the wildernesses of the world as wasted area, to be converted as soon as possible to populated and productive lands. An alternative view, however, has been growing in popularity. The undeveloped areas that we see in this section can be viewed as life reservoirs for the world, places where plants and animals that cannot survive the pressures of industry and agriculture still have a chance to exist. From this point of view, parts of the Amazon basin, the Arctic slopes, coastal Antarctica, central Australia, south Patagonia and the steppes of Asia should be carefully set aside without further development, as objects for preservation and study. We should view them from afar, as with space images, or at least in a way that minimizes the effects of the observer on the terrain. Only in this way, ecologists now argue, can we leave a legacy of unspoiled regions for future generations.

That argument is persuasive, but it neglects one crucial point. The earth's greatest wilderness, its least explored territory, and its biggest reservoir of unknown resources and life-forms, will not be seen in this book. The oceans cover 70 per cent of the globe, an area of 360,000,000 square kilometres (139,000,000 square miles). This is the earth's final frontier, a potential source of food and minerals that dwarfs what the land now provides. Its exploitation by man has scarcely begun, but its abuse as the dumping ground for our wastes is already well advanced. One priority of the next twenty years must be the understanding, protection, and eventually the preservation and management of this final wilderness.

Issyk Kul, Kirgiz Soviet Socialist Republic

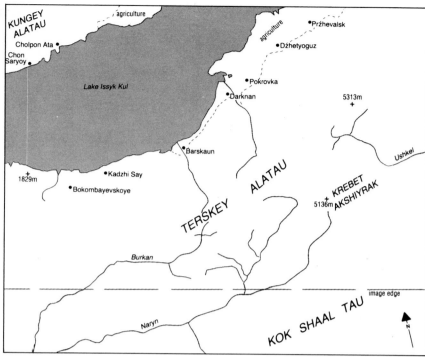

One thousand years ago this part of the world was well known to the nomadic tribes of Tartars who wandered the barren steppes of Central Asia and occasionally erupted into Europe. To them, the great lake seen at the top of the image was familiar as Issyk Kul, the 'warm sea', nestled in a depression of the Tien Shan (the Celestial Mountains). Lake Balkhash, off the image but only 400 kilometres (250 miles) north, is frozen for five months of the year; but Issyk Kul, warmed by this area's volcanic activity, never freezes, although it lies 1,600 metres (5,300 feet) above sea-level.

The image overleaf shows part of Kirgiziya, the Kirgiz Soviet Socialist Republic, in south central U.S.S.R. The border with China is just below the lower right corner of the image. The highest point of the snow-capped mountains that fill the centre of the scene, the 7,400-metre (24,400-foot) Pobedy Peak, is also just outside the image area. Although the area has been populated for thousands of years and has been since Roman times familiar to merchants travelling from China to the West, it was only rediscovered by the western Russians in the last century. Exploration began in 1854, and the region came under central Russian rule in 1876. Since 1936 it has been a constituent union republic.

The lake of Issyk Kul is 6,200 square kilometres (2,400 square miles) in area (ten times the size of Loch Ness) and slightly saline. The result of Pleistocene glaciation, it reaches a depth of 670 metres (2,100 feet). The soils here are like those of the steppes further north, of moderate fertility, but as the plentiful red-displayed vegetation on its banks suggests, the shores of Issyk Kul are a productive agricultural area. However, the mountain ranges to the north and south rise to 5,000 metres (16,000 feet), and so have served to isolate the lake and slow the region's development.

The main range visible on the image is the Terskey Alatau, the 'mottled mountains', so called because of the patches of perennial snow that are scattered over their summits and show prominently on this midsummer scene. A similar range, the Kungey Alatau, lies to the north of the lake. The vegetated foothills of both these ranges provide summer grazing for the livestock that is still the area's principal economic resource. Agriculture, visible in the rectangular fields by the shores of Issyk Kul in the left half of the image, is mainly sugar beets, wheat, opium poppies, tobacco, and southern hemp. The discovery of coal deposits at Kadzhi Say, on the southern shore, provided the first thrust of the area towards modern industry. This is continuing with the development of a shipping line on Issyk Kul, which will run the length of the lake.

Przhevalsk, the area's largest town, produces flour, sunflower oil, wines and beer. Formerly called Karakol, it was renamed in honour of the famous Russian explorer who between 1871 and 1888 made four great trips through Central Asia and China, finally to die at Issyk Kul in 1888 after traversing the ferocious Takla Makan Desert and the Tien Shan mountains that lie south of here.

Image scale and date: 1 cm = 3.9 km, August 1975.

147

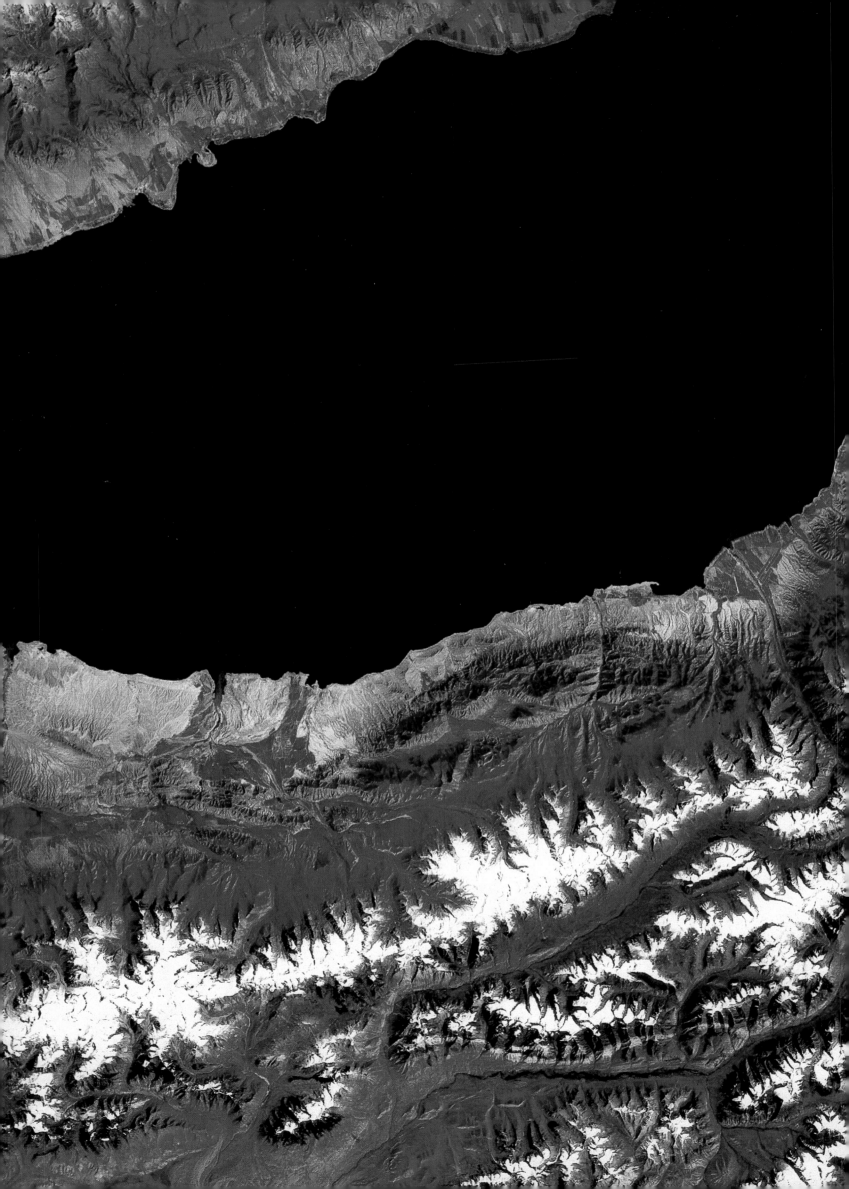

The Everglades and Southern Florida

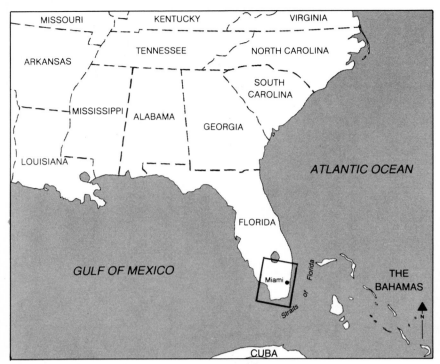

Florida is the United States' most southerly continental state, stretching down almost to the Tropic of Cancer. Close to sea-level, humid and mild in climate, south Florida is the location of the country's largest remaining subtropical wilderness, the Everglades. Seen here as the dark-green red-speckled area in the centre of the image, this great swamp covers over 13,000 square kilometres (5,000 square miles), from Lake Okeechobee just visible in the north to Florida Bay and Cape Sable in the south. The southern part of the Everglades is preserved as a national park, while in the north the swampy area is shrinking as the lands south of the lake are drained and converted to agricultural use.

Most of the Everglades have a substrate of limestone, covered by deep, rotted organic material. Erosion in the limestone has created water-filled sinkholes and springs. They can be seen in the upper left of the image as numerous tiny black dots against a green background of waterlogged soil covered with tough sawgrass. Further south in the Everglades the brightest red patches are 'tree islands', or hammocks, permanent stands of hardwood trees fixed in the slow-moving southward seepage of the swamp.

Once drained, the Everglades produce fertile soils, and the agricultural area south of the town of Belle Glade (seen here as a light blue patch on the shore of Lake Okeechobee) is a highly productive one, providing large crops of sugar cane, citrus fruit, and vegetables. Newly drained and reclaimed farming areas are distinguishable by the whiter tone of the field patterns. Extensive systems of drainage canals have been built in the northern Everglades, and the largest of these are visible on the image. The Hillsboro, North New River, and Miami Canals show up clearly in the upper part of the scene, and further south the Tamiami Canal and the Tamiami Trail

beside it run right across the lower peninsula. Just above the Tamiami Canal the white line of an abandoned airport stands out against the dark-green swamp.

The Everglades merge on the west side with Big Cypress Swamp, the location of an Indian reservation, and then in the south-west we see the broken red coastal strip of the Ten Thousand Islands mangrove flat. This continues all the way to the end of the peninsula, where the dark waters of Ponce de Leon Bay and Whitewater Bay are visible inland from Cape Sable. As the bright blue of the western offshore waters suggests, the Gulf of Mexico is shallow here, and the blue shoals continue round to the east to Florida Bay, the long island chain of the Florida Keys, and Biscayne Bay. On the west side of Biscayne Bay the cooling canals of the Turkey Point nuclear power station appear as a large, greenish-black trapezium.

The line of sand spits and coral reefs runs north past Key Biscayne to meet the mainland at Miami Beach. Inland the light blue patch of Miami can be seen, the region's largest city with a metropolitan-area population of nearly 1.5 million. The mild climate of the eastern seaboard of Florida is famous, and north from Miami an almost continuous line of seaside resort development towns is visible (see map). The soils along this eastern seaboard are mainly sandy dunes of low fertility.

The east coast of Florida is washed by the waters of the Gulf Stream, and over the centuries its warm current has eroded the offshore shelf to create an underwater precipice. The dark waters visible north of Miami increase rapidly in depth; just a few kilometres beyond the shoreline off Delray Beach and Lantana the seabed is hundreds of metres deep.

Image scale and date: 1 cm = 6 km, March 1978.

Southern Patagonia

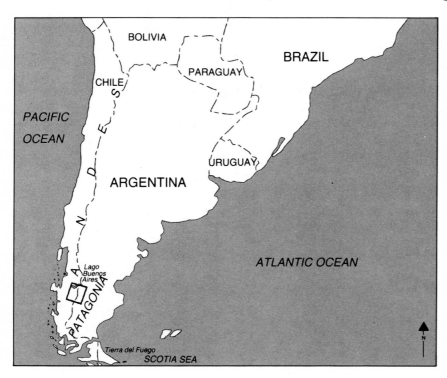

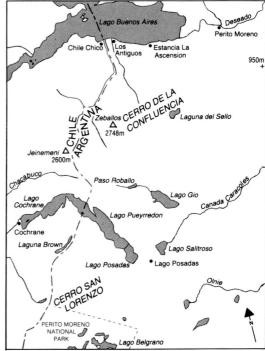

South of Buenos Aires the long South American peninsula continues for almost 2,300 kilometres (1,400 miles), down to the island of Tierra del Fuego. This picture shows a southern portion of it, a western area of Patagonia on the Argentina-Chile border, where the Pacific Ocean washes less than 110 kilometres (70 miles) from the left-hand image boundary. This is the eastern foothills of the Andes, and although the mountain chain is less high here than in the north of the continent, the western part of the image rises in places to 3,700 metres (12,000 feet). The left-hand side of the picture is in Chile's Aisen Province and the right is in Argentina's Santa Cruz Province.

The region is marked by a great series of mountain lakes that runs from Lago Buenos Aires, which stretches for over 100 kilometres (60 miles) across the top of the image, all the way down to Lago Argentino, 240 kilometres (150 miles) south of the picture area. The east-west trending lakes straddle the Argentina-Chile border, so that Lago Buenos Aires is in both countries, as is Lago Pueyrredon (known in Chile as Lago Cochrane), lower down the image. The eastern end of Lago Pueyrredon has yet a third name, Lago Posadas, since there are actually two bodies of water here, separated from each other by a thin bridge of rock. The straight, narrow bridge appears man-made on the image, but it is a natural form. There is also a slight colour difference visible between the two bodies of water, indicating a difference of depth or sedimentation. Lago Gio, further east, shows a clear-cut shoreline that appears to a ground observer as steep-sided, blinding-white cliffs.

Most of Patagonia is a cold desert, deprived of moisture by the barrier of the Andes on the west and by the drying effects of the cold north-flowing Falklands Current on the east. However, the heavy vegetative cover on the left part of this scene makes it clear that there is adequate moisture there. The region's slow development in agriculture and industry is due less to either cold or dryness than to the strong westerly winds, which blow incessantly from the Cordillera of the Andes across the hills and plains at speeds of more than 110 kilometres (70 miles) an hour. Early explorers labelled Lago Buenos Aires the 'Kingdom of the Winds'. Streaks on the blue-grey and brown plateau areas to the right of Lago Belgrano and Lago Pueyrredon show that the gusting winds are almost due east-west.

The marked difference in colours between the two sides of the picture reflect altitude and rainfall differences. The east is dry and dusty, with only thornbush and tough grass on the dark surface of old volcanic flows; the west is tall flowering grasses, thickets, and forests of cypress, redwood, and Antarctic beech, seen in this spring image partly covered by snow on the higher hills. In the southern part of the scene, around Lago Belgrano, these woods are part of the Perito Moreno National Park.

Although this region, like the rest of Patagonia, is under-developed, a couple of hundred years ago it was a magnet for explorers. The legendary city of Trapalanda, the 'City of the Caesars', was reputed to be here, an El Dorado of jewels and gold. It was said to lie somewhere in the Andes, with a latitude of about 47 degrees – just about at Paso Roballo, in the centre of this image. Today the area is a magnet again, this time for geologists who seek the more base metals of copper, lead, zinc, and chromium in the Andean foothills, which are hoped will match Chilean deposits found further north.

Image scale and date: 1 cm = 6 km, November 1973.

Manaus and the Amazon

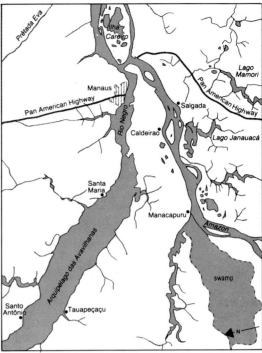

The Amazon is indisputably the world's greatest river. Draining a basin that covers 40 per cent of South America and has an area of over 5.8 million square kilometres (2.3 million square miles), the Amazon delivers 3,300,000,000,000 gallons of water a day to the Atlantic Ocean — 15 per cent of the fresh water delivered to all the oceans by all the world's rivers, ten times the flow of the Mississippi, four times as much as the Zaire (Congo) River. Its watershed is drawn partly from the Andes, the width of a continent away. It is wide and deep enough to permit passage of ocean steamers of 4 metres (14 foot) draft as far as Iquitos in Peru, over 2,500 kilometres (1,600 miles) from its Atlantic estuary.

This image shows the great river at the junction with one of its major tributaries, the Rio Negro, 1,200 kilometres (750 miles) from the Amazon's mouth. The two rivers do not completely mingle, but retain their separate colours for many kilometres past their confluence, right to the edge of the picture. The Amazon, as its blue tone suggests, carries far more sediment with it than the Rio Negro. Swirling vegetated mudflats are visible in the black Rio Negro on the left of the scene, and in the lower right corner of the picture there is a complex pattern of swamp, dark lakes, and black threads of waterways connecting into the Amazon.

The city of Manaus stands just 3 degrees south of the equator, on the northern bank of the Rio Negro a few kilometres before its meeting with the Amazon. It is visible here as a bright patch of blue-white to the left of the dark river. Manaus, established back in the seventeenth century, has a strange history. Originally an Indian slave centre, in the last quarter of the nineteenth century it enjoyed an enormous boom period as the centre for the collection and shipping of wild rubber. Many great buildings were constructed, including the spectacular waterfront Opera House. When rubber seeds were smuggled out of Brazil in 1876 and East Indian plantation rubber became available early this century the economy of Manaus collapsed.

Now the city has begun to grow again, part of the general development of Brazil's interior. For three centuries the only channel of communication with Manaus was along the river. Steamship service to Belém, at the Amazon's mouth, was introduced in 1857 to provide a reliable form of transport, but it was on an infrequent basis. Today, jungle roads, clearly visible on the image, strike out north and south from Manaus. The Pan American Highway is prominent as a white line in the upper half of the image, part of the new highway system that is being created in central Brazil. Manaus is the commercial hub for this vast central area of the Amazon Basin, exporting rubber, jute, Brazil nuts, and rosewood oil. A large refinery at Manaus processes Peruvian petroleum, carried down the river from Pucallpa, 1,900 kilometres (1,200 miles) away to the south-west. Beef and hides are imported from the area of Rio Branco, a northern tributary of the Rio Negro, and then shipped east along the river. Air services now exist to all parts of Brazil.

Most of this scene is covered by the continuous red-displayed vegetation of the Amazon rain forest. Several separate vertical layers of growth in the forest, plus a deep forest carpet, make the soil surface quite invisible. However, like most rain-forest soils it is leached of minerals and poor in fertility. Cleared white and green areas can be seen in the jungle, usually flanking the new roads which provide the only easy access, but they have limited productivity. The main crops for local consumption are corn, beans, peppers, peanuts, and especially cassava.

Image scale and date: 1 cm = 5.9 km, July 1977.

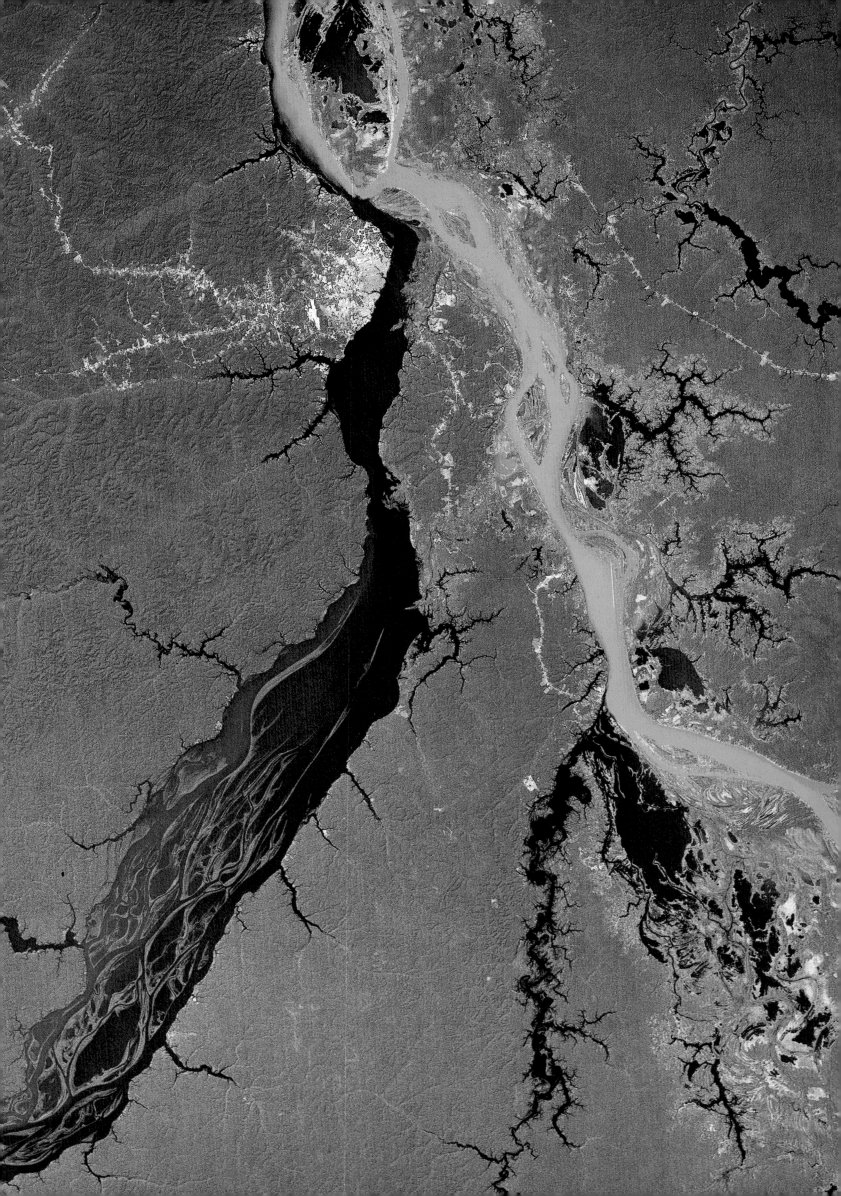

Anchorage and South Alaska

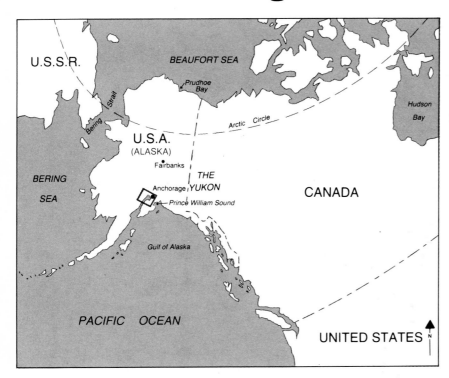

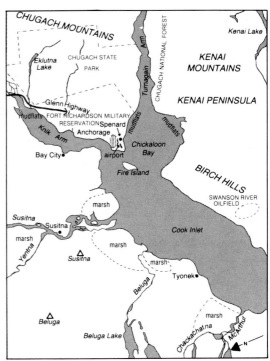

In describing Western Australia earlier in the book the point was made that the state is greatly under-populated, with only 1 million people in an area of 2.5 million square kilometres. Alaska suffers a worse version of the same problem, with only 350,000 people in 1,519,000 square kilometres (586,000 square miles). In this case the difficulty is accentuated by the harsh climate of much of the state, and so despite the vast natural resources of the region its development has been rather slow.

This image area covers part of the southern shore of mainland Alaska, including the city of Anchorage, home for more than half the population of the state. With warmth and moisture provided by the warm Alaska Current, the climate here is far different from the popular notion of Alaska as a perennially cold Arctic desert. Anchorage, at 61 degrees north, has about the same latitude as Oslo, Helsinki, or Leningrad, and a more temperate climate than the latter two cities.

The broad blue swath running up the image centre is Cook Inlet, shallow and sediment-laden, which empties south of the scene area into the Gulf of Alaska. Anchorage lies on a peninsula jutting down into Cook Inlet, and the blue patch of the city is prominent there. The Glenn Highway can be seen running to the left from the city to meet the Richardson Highway and the Alaskan Highway to Fairbanks beyond the image area. The airport shows clearly at the end of the peninsula, with the red comma of Fire Island a few miles offshore. The darker tones within the bright blue water are mudflats, most noticeable to the right of Anchorage and along the length of the Turnagain Arm, an inlet which cuts

through almost to Prince William Sound (off the image to the east).

Birch Hills on the lower part of the Kenai Peninsula show as a flat, glaciated plain, peppered by the black specks of numerous clear lakes. Although now overshadowed by the great oilfields of Prudhoe Bay on Alaska's North Slope, the first commercial find in the state was made here in 1957, in the Swanson River field near the upper shore of Cook Inlet towards the right-hand edge of the picture. This field held about 450 million barrels, in a stratum between 3,000 and 3,500 metres (10,000 and 11,500 feet) below the surface. On the lower edge of the peninsula, the refinery and tanker terminal for the oilfield show as blue specks at the right-hand edge of the scene.

Further up the reddish-brown and black part of the Kenai Peninsula lie the brighter red and blue-grey folds of the Kenai Mountains with the Chugach National Forest on the left side of them. Above Anchorage the snow-covered Chugach Mountain area is preserved as a state park. The mountains rise to 2,400 metres (8,000 feet) at the top left-hand corner of the scene, and much of the spruce, Alaskan cedar and Western red cedar here is stunted and of limited commercial value.

Below Cook Inlet much of the land shows the pale pinkish-brown and greens of marshy areas (muskeg), particularly near the mouths of the Beluga and Susitna rivers and in the area between the Susitna and Yentna rivers. The snow and cloud-capped peak of Mount Susitna (1,300 metres; 4,400 feet) shows a brighter red among the marshes, and at the bottom edge of the picture lie the bright blue-and-white snow and glaciers of the foothills of the Alaska Range.

Image scale and date: 1 cm = 5.6 km, August 1978.

The Takla Makan Desert and K2, China

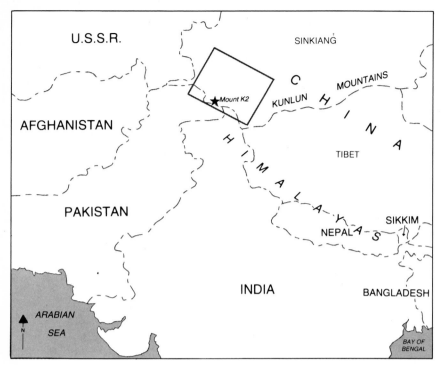

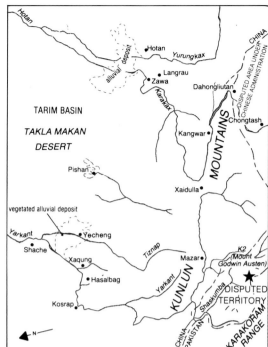

About one-fifth of the world's land surface cannot be cultivated because it is too dry. Another fifth cannot grow crops because it is too high and covered with bare rock. This image, in western China's Sinkiang (Xinjiang) Province, is a good combination of the two. On the left side lies the western end of the Takla Makan Desert, while bottom right are the peaks of the Karakoram Range, part of the great Alpine-Himalayan chain that runs unbroken from North Africa and Western Europe to Java and the Lesser Sunda Islands. Neither desert nor mountain range offers fertile ground or the possibility of extensive plant, animal or human life.

The scene is a composite of a dozen different Landsat images and covers a great range of altitudes from the desert plain 1.5 kilometres (1 mile) above sea-level on the left to peaks more than 8 kilometres (5 miles) above sea-level on the right. K2 (Mount Godwin Austen), in the lower right of the image, is at 8,611 metres (28,250 feet) the world's second highest mountain, and was not scaled until a successful attempt by an Italian expedition in 1954. The area around K2 is shown in more detail in the enlarged image on page 1 of this book. The mountain lies in the disputed area between Pakistan and China in the bottom right-hand corner of the picture, and displays the thin blue ribbons of glaciers descending from the highest peaks.

To the left of the mountains the Takla Makan has long been recognized as one of the world's largest (337,000 square kilometres; 130,000 square miles) and most extreme deserts. In ancient times this region was part of High Tartary, also known as Chinese Tartary and Chinese Turkestan. Travellers along the Great Silk Road, carrying silk, gold, spices, coral, amber, lacquer, ceramics, inventions, and rare plants and animals to Europe, knew and feared this desert nearly 2,000 years ago. Marco Polo, who travelled across it in 1224, referred to its 'ghoul-infested deserts', and the name itself, Takla Makan, means 'Go in and you won't come out'. Here in its western part the land is a little less hostile, with the north-flowing streams of the Hotan and Yarkant rivers breaking the flat tan pattern of the dunes and showing patches of vegetation along their courses. Except in the mountains, the rainfall is still negligible at 1–5 centimetres (0·5–2 inches) a year. The natural vegetation consists of only shrubs and marsh plants in the damp stream beds. The few oases, such as Hotan and Shache, cluster on the northern slopes of the mountains, where cultivated alluvial areas can be seen, and the rivers, flowing north from the Kunlun Mountains, are often absorbed into the desert and disappear in the sands and shifting dunes. The Hotan River, for example, reaches its northern destination of the Tarim River on average only forty days of the year.

This barren region might seem to be of little economic interest and potential, but that is not the case. Many foreign groups would welcome an opportunity to investigate it in detail. The area forms part of the Tarim Basin, and is regarded as one of China's promising new areas for oil and gas exploration.

Image scale and dates: 1 cm = 17.1 km, 1972–1979.

Index